The new design of the exhibitions was undertaken by the House of Bavarian History in cooperation with the Dachau Concentration Camp Memorial Site and the Comité International de Dachau and in consultation with the expert advisory board.

Project direction

Dr. habil. Ludwig Eiber, Dr. Manfred Treml
(1998-2000), Prof. Dr. Claus Grimm (2000-2003)

Curatorial and authorial team

Dr. h.c. Barbara Distel
Exhibit selection and responsible author
for sections:
1, 6.1-6.9, 13.6, 13.7

Dr. habil. Ludwig Eiber
Exhibit selection and responsible author for
the information panels in the "Schubraum" and
prisoner baths as well as sections:
3.1-3.4, 4.1-4.7, 4.12-15, 5.6, 7.12, 7.26, 8.3,
8.4, 8.6, 9.0, 9.3, 9.4, 9.5, 9.7, 9.9, 9.10, 10.2D,
10.4, 11.3, 11.4, 12.5, 13.1, 13.2, 13.5

Thomas Felsenstein
Exhibit selection and responsible author
for sections:
7.24, 7.25, 8.2, 9.1, 9.8, 9.11, 10.0-10.2C, 10.5
(10 with Wolfgang Kucera), 12.4

Dr. Gabriele Hammermann
Exhibit selection and responsible author
for sections:
3.7-3.10, 5.1-5.5, 5.7, 5.9, 5.10, 8.5, 9.6, 13.3, 13.4

Micha Neher
Exhibit selection and responsible author
for sections:
7.3, 7.10, 7.11, 7.13, 7.15, 7.17, 7.18, 7.19, 7.20,
7.22, 7.23

Dr. Christian Schölzel
Exhibit selection and responsible for sections:
2.1-2.10, 9.1, 9.2, 10.3, 13.1, 13.5

Dr. Stanislav Zámečník
Exhibit selection and responsible for sections:
3.5-3.6, 4.8-4.11, 5.8, 7.1, 7.2, 7.4-7.9, 7.11,
7.14, 7.16, 7.19, 7.21, 7.22, 8.1, 11.1, 11.2, 11.5,
12.1-12.3, 12.6

www.comiteinternationaldachau.com

The Dachau Concentration Camp, 1933 to 1945

Text and photo documents
from the exhibition, with CD

Foreword from the President of the International Dachau Committee

Sixty years after the liberation of the Dachau concentration camp our ranks have thinned dramatically. Our testimony for coming generations is therefore gaining in importance. An integral part of this is the Memorial Site of the former Dachau concentration camp, which was created on our initiative and based on our ideas in 1965. The catalogue to the 1965 exhibition, published in German, English, French and Italian, found great resonance among both German and international visitors to the Memorial Site for many decades. They took the survivors' message with them back home.

In 2003 a new documentary exhibition was opened which reflects the latest historical research on the history of the Dachau concentration camp. Former prisoners of the Dachau camp worked on this exhibition, but in contrast to 1965 they no longer bore sole responsibility.

However, the survivors of the Dachau concentration camp, joined together in the International Committee, have brought out this catalog on the new exhibition together with the Dachau Concentration Camp Memorial Site. The catalog is comprised of two parts: a book containing the most important and vivid photos and documents from the new exhibition, and a CD encompassing all of the texts and documents in the exhibition. We hope that this will do justice to the varied interests of visitors.

At the same time, this catalog shall also serve an urgent concern of the former prisoners: it shall document to future generations what the prisoners were forced to go through between 1933 and 1945.

The catalog is to contribute to keeping humankind from repeating a similar disaster.

In January 2005

General André Delpech (France) on behalf of all survivors of the Dachau concentration camp

Contents

	Page		Section

Contents

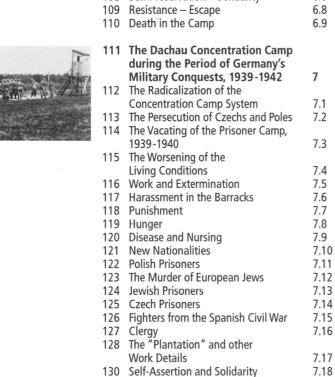

Contents

Essays

Jürgen Zarusky
From Weimar to Dachau: The Destruction of Democracy and its Consequences

On March 22, 1933, the Dachau concentration camp was opened on the grounds of an unused munitions factory from the First World War. On the evening of April 10, the SS took over the guarding of the prisoners from the Bavarian police. Only two days later, on April 12, the first deaths followed: four prisoners were led out of the gates and shot while allegedly "trying to escape". On April 25, four men were put under detention in the camp prison, known as the "bunker", which had only just been fitted out. Three of them were driven to commit suicide or shot; Hans Beimler, a Communist Reichstag deputy, managed to escape. Six more prisoners died in May. "Shot while trying to escape", "shot in self-defense", or "suicide" – these were the causes of death cited by the SS. The majority of those murdered were of Jewish ancestry.

A battlefield scene from World War I

The cause of death cited by the SS and the camp doctor did not always stand up to the findings of the judicial autopsy: in some cases it was simply not possible to cover up the markings of extremely brutal torture. On June 1, 1933, the head state prosecutor at the Munich II district court, Karl Wintersberger, brought charges of murder in four cases. Immediately afterwards, the Justice Ministry demanded the investigation files for the purpose of discussing the incidents at the governmental level. It then passed them on to the Interior Ministry for an opinion. There, the Political Police Commissioner – none other than Heinrich Himmler, who was also in charge of the SS and the Dachau concentration camp – allegedly never received the files, as he claimed after months of delaying tactics. The murders went unpunished and the prisoners in the concentration camp were left without any protection from a state in which the rule of law, reduced to an absurdity, had been destroyed.

This was the beginning of a development in which over 200,000 persons from across Europe were robbed of their freedom, tortured and exploited in the Dachau concentration camp and its subcamps.

Some 40,000 prisoners died violently at the hands of the SS, as well as from starvation and sheer exhaustion, from a lack of medical care and epidemics. And all this was a mere fraction of the murderous dynamic let loose by the Nazi regime in the twelve years of its existence.

How could this have happened? Why did millions of voters and a host of supporters, from SA thugs to bankers, contribute to heaving Hitler to the threshold of power, and in doing so not only destroy the first German democracy, but also the rule of law? Debate on this issue has continued for decades. Here we can present only a few of the key factors that determined the fateful course Germany took at that time.

The burdens of the First World War

The first factor we need to consider are the consequences of the First World War, during which well over eight million people were violently killed and an even greater number left physically and emotionally crippled. There can be no doubt that mass death in a positional war fought with modern weapons, including poison gas, damaged contemporaries' feeling for the value of human life.

That military thinking continued to have an effect on far too many veterans, and indeed radicalized further, was not in the first instance, as is often claimed, due to the severity of the victorious powers. That the Versailles Treaty of June 1919 was neither an act of political wisdom nor particularly just, was already pointed out by unbiased contemporary critics like the British economist John Maynard Keynes and the Social-Democratic Second International. Loss of large chunks of territory, enormous reparation payments, and tight restrictions placed on German military power were certainly not easy to digest, and there was hardly anyone in Germany who could see anything positive in the settlement. One did not have to be a National Socialist to criticize it.

Of significance for the rise of right wing extremism and its subsequent establishment on the political scene was not so much the Versailles Treaty, but a chaotic web made up of a denial of reality and the living of political lies, in which right wing extremists, conservatives, and even a considerable section of the political center became entangled when facing the lost war. The military leadership contributed greatly to this, for right up till September 1918 it had continually announced its unshakeable belief that victory could be achieved, but then after heavy defeats and the defections of its allies had to acknowledge that the situation was hopeless. It now took the bull by the horns, which was at the same time a way of avoiding responsibility. The supreme command of the armed forces under Field Marshal Paul von Hindenburg and General Erich Ludendorff not only demanded that Kaiser Wilhelm II immediately commence armistice negotiations, but also turn the Reich into a parliamentary democracy. These demands made of the Kaiser were not raised solely to achieve better armistice conditions from US President Wilson. This strategy was also intended to shift responsibility for dealing with the disaster brought about by the supreme command to the Reichstag majority, a coalition of Social Democrats, the Catholic Center Party, and the left-liberal Progress Party, which had jointly demanded democratic reforms and the commencement of negotiations for ending the war since 1917. Their calculations did not work out entirely however, for, as the navy command sought to sabotage the armistice negotiations by sending out the fleet one last time, sailors rebelled, quickly igniting a revolution that led to the collapse of the brittle Wilhelminian German Reich. Germany became a republic.

The November Revolution was the result of defeat in war, but the political right wing confused cause and effect. They believed that it was not the hopeless military situation that had led to capitulation, but a "stab in the back" of the fighting front by the home front. The war weariness of broad sectors of the population, also expressed repeatedly from 1917 in a series of strikes, was interpreted as a treacherous conspiracy. Those propagating the legend of the "stab in the back" were not sparing in their accusations of guilt: their accusing finger was directed mainly at Socialists and Jews. An atmosphere of anti-Semitism had already spread during the war. In 1916, the War Ministry had pursued slanderous claims put into circulation by anti-Semites directed against allegedly shirking Jews. It counted the number of Jews in the German Army, ignoring the energetic protests of Social Democrats, Liberals and Jewish organizations against this discriminating measure. The results were subsequently kept secret, however, because they did not verify the anti-Semitic expectations. The legend of a "stab in the back" enjoyed broad acceptance throughout society. In the fall of 1919 it was even propagated by Paul von Hindenburg, who of course knew better, before a parliamentary commission of inquiry. Almost six years later, in 1925, a broad right wing coalition – ranging from the still insignificant National Socialists and the ultra nationalists to the Catholic Bavarian People's Party – supported von Hindenburg's accession to the office of Reich President, defeating the candidate of the democratic political parties, Wilhlem Marx of the Catholic Center Party. The "stab-in-the-back" legend not only poisoned the political climate of the Weimar Republic, but also continued to reverberate in the terror judgments passed by the National Socialist People's Courts against resistance fighters in the 1930s and 1940s, which stated time and again that the accused had to be punished severely so as to avoid a repetition of November 1918.

Corresponding to the "stab-in-the-back" legend was the "lie of war guilt". This was also deeply anchored in society and enjoyed official support. That Germany bore no or at least no primary responsibility for the outbreak of the First World War was to be proven in a number of ways, including the official Foreign Office files, which were then unabashedly edited or falsified. Anyone seeking to reveal what had in fact gone on faced great diffi-

Hindenburg, Wilhelm II, Ludendorff

culties, indeed they exposed themselves to life-threatening danger, as the case of Felix Fechenbach shows. As personal assistant to Bavarian Minister President Kurt Eisner, who was installed in office during the Revolution and subsequently murdered in February 1919, Fechenbach was involved in the publication of files which proved the war-mongering attitude of the German government in the summer of 1914. In scandalous circumstances a Bavarian court sentenced him to twelve years imprisonment for treason in October 1922, and he was not pardoned until the end of 1924, after a massive campaign was mobilized on his behalf. In the end though, Fechenbach paid for his political struggle against blind nationalism with his life: after the National Socialists seized power he was taken into "protective custody" and shot on a transport heading for the Dachau concentration camp in August 1933.

Lack of a fundamental consensus

The Weimar Republic, founded in 1919 and named after the venue of the Constituent National Assembly, lacked a unifying fundamental consensus. From the very beginning, powerful political forces contested its legitimacy. The first challenge was issued by the left wing of the November Revolution, namely the Spartacus Alliance, the revolutionary union stewards, and radical currents in the Independent Social Democratic Party founded in 1917, all of whom sought to turn the spontaneously formed workers' councils into the basis of a Marxist "dictatorship of the proletariat." From January to May 1919 there was a series of leftist uprisings, from the Spartacus rebellion in Berlin to the Bavarian Councils' Republic, which the Social Democrat dominated government put down with the help of military and paramilitary units known as the Freikorps. The political forces supporting parliamentary democracy, who rejected every form of dictatorship and rightly feared that if they did not stop the leftist radicals then the danger of civil war would become manifest, ultimately asserted their authority, albeit at a high

price. The socialist workers' movement emerged from the revolution deeply divided; Social Democrats and Communists were locked in a bitter struggle. This division between democratic and dictatorial socialism ran so deep that it even proved unbridgeable as they were faced with a common enemy, National Socialism. But, initially, it was the Freikorps who were able to make their mark and establish themselves as custodians of order, even if as a rule they were anything but loyal to the Republic. Many of the Freikorps, for instance those involved in the quelling of the Munich Councils' Republic and the subsequent massacre of the "Reds", had already marked their helmets with the swastika.

The first attempted coup d'etat from the right followed quickly. In March 1920, the East Prussian landowner and civil servant Wolfgang Kapp and General Walther von Lüttwitz launched a putsch, only to fail because of a hurriedly called general strike. While in the Ruhr area the resistance of the workforce grew into a radical leftist revolt, which was brutally suppressed, in Bavaria Johannes Hoffmann's Social Democratic minority government was pressured into resigning by the paramilitary units and conservative politicians. Under his successor, Gustav Ritter von Kahr, there was a significant swing to the right and Bavaria became an el dorado for extremist right wing militias and lynch-law killers. Adolf Hitler's NSDAP also flourished in this political climate. Attempting to imitate Mussolini's march on Rome with a dilettantish putsch in November of the crisis year 1923, Hitler ended up before an extremely lenient judge of the Bavarian People's Court instead of in the chancellor's office in Berlin, followed by a few months in Landsberg prison, where he dictated his book Mein Kampf while enjoying very comfortable conditions. Besides the partially falsified autobiographical details, this crude, devilish work also formulates the irrational ideological mishmash, drenched with hatred, which constituted the "intellectual" fuel of the Nazis: Social Darwinism, racism, anti-Semitism, militarism, the

Poster propagating the "stab-in-the-back" legend

Fuehrer principle, and an imperialism that directed its attention to eastern Europe (motto: "living space in the East"). The lesson Hitler drew from this failed putsch was that the path for realizing this program had to lead through the Republic's institutions.

While the luxury treatment granted to the traitor Adolf Hitler, who although not a German citizen was allowed to remain in the country and continue his political career, was certainly only conceivable in the Bavaria of these years, it was nonetheless symptomatic of the overall situation. In the 1920s Emil Julius Gumbel, a mathematics lecturer from Heidelberg, proved statistically in several publications that hundreds of political murders committed by right wing extremists remained unpunished or were punished with ridiculously light penalties; on the other hand, the political murders committed by leftists, although considerably fewer in number, received the full force of the law. Although only an insignificant number of civil servants had refused to swear allegiance to the new Reich constitution, putting their positions on the line in doing so, the instances of false swearing of oaths in Germany was probably never higher than in 1919, the year the constitution was adopted. A large number of civil servants, in particular in the judiciary, never inwardly broke with the authoritarian Wilhelminian Reich and discharged their duties accordingly. The same applied to the military, which remained loyal only as long it was a matter of suppressing left wing revolution. In 1920 during the Kapp Putsch, however, the Reich Army refused to protect the legitimate government. General Hans von Seeckt, who used the motto "soldiers do not shoot soldiers" to position himself as the leader of the disloyal troops, did not suffer any consequences for his stance. On the contrary, shortly afterwards he was promoted from chief of the troop bureau to chief of army command.

The new democracy in Germany could only count on very limited support from the state apparatus, but even more fateful was that the citizenry was also no guarantee of democratic rule. The parties of the so-called Weimar Coalition, the Socialist Party, the Center and the left-liberal German Democratic Party, lost the majority they had held in the National Assembly as early as the first Reichstag elections in 1920. The Council of People's Delegates, the revolutionary interim government made up of representatives from the Socialist Party and the more left wing-oriented Independent Socialist Party, had introduced women's suffrage and lowered the voting age from 25 to 20 in 1919. Civic equality between the sexes was also anchored in the Weimar constitution. Too few appreciated the chances that the extension of political participation had opened up. Nevertheless, this was an achievement of the republic, and certainly not the only one. The republic had coped with the reintegration of millions of war veterans into civilian life, and it had survived the political assaults from the right and the left in the immediate postwar years as well as the hyperinflation of 1923. In terms of culture, the first German republic witnessed years of unprecedented creativity, the richness of which can only be indicated here in a few sentences: New Objectivity in pictorial arts with such important artists as Otto Dix, Max Beckmann and Christian Schad should be mentioned; in literature there were works such as Thomas Mann's The Magic Mountain, Alfred Döblin's Berlin Alexanderplatz, Erich Maria Remarque's All Quiet on the Western Front, and a host of others, as well as Bertold Brecht's epic theatre, whose dramatic beginning was marked by The Three-penny Opera; and music witnessed the rise of Arnold Schönberg's twelve-tone music and the burgeoning triumph of jazz. However, the opponents of cultural modernity often utilized defamations tainted with anti-Semitic prejudices, such as "cultural Bolshevism" and "gutter literature".

From the complex position of an inferior and humiliated war opponent, and in spite of the rampant political irrationalism, the foundations of a rapprochement policy with the West (but not with

Scene from the November 1923 Hitler Putsch BaySB

Poland!) were laid in the middle years of the Weimar Republic, a step chiefly associated with the name of Gustav Stresemann. Stresemann was in no way an enthusiastic supporter of the republic, but enough of a realist to undertake a constructive foreign policy within the given circumstances. For all the essential steps of his policy towards the West he relied on support from the Social Democrats, who then duly provided it from the opposition benches. As chancellor from 1923 and then as foreign minister until his death in 1929, Stresemann was also an element of stability in a republic characterized by a deficient political culture, which saw sixteen governments alone between 1919 and 1930. In material terms, the "golden years" of the Weimar Republic, lasting from 1924 to 1928, were not really that rosy for most citizens, but at least one important social policy reform was introduced in 1927, the unemployment benefit, which, however, was incapable of alleviating the burdens of the mass unemployment triggered soon afterwards by the worldwide economic crisis.

The crisis of the Great Depression ended fatally for democracy in Germany. The economic problems did not by any means have to inevitably lead to a dictatorship. Other European countries or for instance the severely shaken USA managed to recover by remaining democracies. In Germany the situation was different because democracy was not so deeply rooted and the shaky consensus that had sustained the republic had steadily eroded. Especially in industrialist circles there were calls for nullifying the influence of the labor movement and replacing the democratic with an authoritarian system. This new course became clear during the Ruhr iron workers strike of 1928-29, as the industrialists instigated wage negotiations with a mass lockout of 200,000 workers and then refused to accept a moderate state arbitration ruling. It was continued in a crisis that signaled the end of Hermann Müller's (SPD) grand coalition government, which collapsed in the spring of 1930, seemingly due to a dispute over raising contributions

The unemployed wait

to unemployment benefits by half a percent. In fact however, it was the confrontational course pursued by the German People's Party, which had close ties to the industrialists and which shifted significantly to the right after the death of its chairman Stresemann, that brought down the government.

The end of the republic

When new elections were held following the end of the Müller government in September 1930, the Great Depression was already entering its eleventh month, having begun in October 1929. Germany had been hard hit: the number of businesses going bankrupt was on the increase and unemployment had risen dramatically. But there was one winner: Adolf Hitler and his NSDAP. Previously receiving three per cent of the vote and figuring merely as a splinter group, the National Socialists had great success and suddenly attained 18.3 per cent of the vote and 107 of the 577 seats in the Reichstag. After the Social Democrats, the Nazis were now the second strongest political party. The distribution of seats in the Reichstag made it impossible to form a workable parliamentary majority, and the new Reich Chancellor Brüning (Center) governed on the basis of the Reich President's power to issue emergency decrees. Conservative circles, such as the strongly right wing-leaning agricultural lobby and the industrialists, saw this not as a temporary solution but as the first step towards replacing the despised parliamentary system with some sort of authoritarian order. For its part, faced with the threat of Nazi electoral success and the need to secure its coalition with the Center Party in Prussia, the largest state in the Reich, the SPD saw itself forced to tolerate the crisis-exacerbating, cost-cutting policies pursued by Brüning. The democratic forces now had very little political room to maneuver, not least because liberalism practically disappeared from the scene and the Catholic Center Party under Monsignor Ludwig Kaas, who had assumed the position of party chairman in 1928, took an increasingly right wing authoritarian line and even momentarily flirted with the idea of forming a coalition with the NSDAP. For three years, from 1930 to 1933, the first German republic writhed in its death throes. Just how desperate the situation had already become in the spring of 1932 is highlighted by the fact that in the presidential elections the democratic parties, including the SPD, supported Hindenburg, against whom they had campaigned bitterly in 1925 and who was in the meantime an old man, solely to prevent Hitler from claiming the office. Hindenburg, however, resentfully held it against Brüning, his campaign strategist, that he owed his office to the "socialists", and duly replaced him as chancellor with the ultraconservative Catholic nobleman Franz von Papen. Although only in office for a few months, von Papen contributed greatly to the destruction of the constitutional order, above all in how, on July 20, 1932, he deposed the Prussian minority government of the SPD and Center Party and installed a commissioner to rule over that state. Resistance to this cold coup d'état, which tore down the most important remaining bastion of democracy, was limited to a complaint submitted to the constitutional court. The more activist Social Democrats hoped for a general strike, but were disappointed. The strike was a blunt weapon in times of massive unemployment. Immediately after the "Prussian blow", the National Socialists became the strongest party in the Reichstag, gaining over 37 per cent of the vote. In contrast to the other parties of the Weimar Republic, the NSDAP was not tied to a specific social class or milieu and its contradictory ideology exerted a broad appeal, addressing the most divergent political needs and wishes. Above all however, the Nazi Party understood how to mobilize anxieties and resentments and exploit them for its own purposes. Although its party headquarters were still located in Munich, the Nazis now found its mass of voters and supporters in the Protestant areas of northern and eastern Germany, mainly amongst the rural and small-town middle class,

threatened with social decline. Other groups the Nazis appealed to were unorganized laborers in small-scale businesses and a considerable segment of the upper strata of society, including the old nobility.

The political conflict in these crisis years was increasingly accompanied by violence. On the streets and in the large assembly halls of the cities, it was mainly members of the Nazi and Communist paramilitary organizations, the SA and Red Front, and occasionally the Social Democrat dominated "Black-Red-Gold Reichsbanner", who got involved in brawls and sometimes real battles, during which hundreds of activists lost their lives. A particularly brutal murder was committed on August 10, 1932 in Potempa, Upper Silesia. There five SA men broke into the apartment of Konrad Pietzuch, an unemployed Communist sympathizer and Polish national, surprising him in his sleep. They then shot and wounded him before literally trampling him to death in front of his mother. In the same night an emergency decree against political violence went into effect which prescribed the death penalty for political murders. It was subsequently applied to Pietzuch's murderers by a special court in Beuthen.

The National Socialists were enraged: a wave of attacks was launched against Jewish businesses and the editorial offices of SPD and Center Party newspapers in Silesia. What really caused a stir, however, was that the party leader Adolf Hitler expressed his unreserved solidarity with the condemned men, declaring that he felt "united with them in limitless loyalty." A week later the Reich government reprieved the murderers, commuting their sentences to life imprisonment, not the least to ensure that not all their ties with the right would be severed. Shortly after Hitler's assumption of power, the murderers, like many other violent Nazi criminals, were granted an amnesty. After the Potempa incident and Hitler's declaration of solidarity with the murderers there could no longer be any illusions as to what the NSDAP and its leader were capable of.

Election poster, 1932

Social Democrats and
Communists taken into
"protective custody"

The seemingly unstoppable rise of the NSDAP suddenly appeared to come to a shuddering halt in the summer of 1932. In the November elections that year they lost 4 percentage points. But in contrast to the Communist Party, which was also profiting from the crisis and, following Stalin's orders, had embarked on an ultra-radical course, the NSDAP was not isolated. The Nazi Party had alliance partners and was itself attractive as an alliance partner for the archconservative opponents of the republic, precisely because, unlike the conservatives, the Nazis understood how to mobilize the masses. Hitler though refused to enter into any coalition in which he would not assume the office of Reich chancellor. On January 30, 1933, his wish was fulfilled by Reich President Hindenburg, who gave in to the machinating influence of von Papen and his own son Oskar. As spokesmen for an agrarian-industrialist power cartel, they believed that they could harness Hitler and his followers, exploiting them for their own restorative purposes. The opposite turned out to be the case: often called the "master rider", von Papen turned out to be nothing more than Hitler's "stirrup", helping him come to power. Not only

was the already undermined republic destroyed in a flash under Hitler's leadership, but also, and above all, the still existing rule of law. As the Reichstag went up in flames on the night of February 27-28, 1933, the National Socialists undertook to exploit this incident for propaganda purposes, claiming it be the signal for an imminent Communist revolt. On the same night the National Socialist leadership ordered the arrest of all Communist functionaries and parliamentarians. On February 28, Hindenburg signed the so-called Reichstag Fire Decree, which remained in force right up to the last day of the Third Reich. Its very first paragraphs suspended all of the basic constitutional rights of citizens, thus legitimizing police custody ("protective custody") for indefinite periods, and, ultimately, the setting up of concentration camps.

The jurist and resistance fighter Ernst Fraenkel has rightly called this document suspending basic civil freedoms the constitutional charter of the Third Reich. The system of concentration camps, with its nucleus in Dachau, became a central element of the new order.

Stanislav Zámečník
The Dachau Concentration Camp in the System of the National Socialist Dictatorship

The concentration camps were an integral component of the National Socialist apparatus of repression. They enabled a restriction of personal freedoms that evaded judicial procedures, and included the use of medieval torture methods, as well as the physical liquidation of practically anyone. Without the concentration camps Himmler's Gestapo could never have developed into a powerful terror organization whose mere mention sufficed to arouse fear and horror.

The Reichstag fire (February 28, 1933) was the trigger for mass arrests. The prisons were quickly overfilled, so that the prisoners were placed in other buildings and grounds deemed suitable, which were later called concentration camps. These were mostly administered by the police, but guard duty at the majority of these sites was performed by members of the SA and SS, who were appointed to the status of auxiliary police and took advantage of the situation to settle scores with their political opponents.

On March 22, 1933, the Dachau concentration camp was officially opened. According to a press release issued by the newly appointed Munich Police President, Heinrich Himmler, it was erected as the "first state concentration camp" with a capacity for approx. 5,000 prisoners. Initially it stood under the administration of the Bavarian State Police, but already on April 10, 1933, an SS unit took over the running of the camp and immediately began installing its rule of terror.

Dachau was not the first concentration camp in Germany. But in contrast to the other camps, which served as provisional arrangements, it was set up as a state concentration camp, as a permanent facility of the Bavarian State. In contrast to the spontaneous, elementary terror that prevailed in the other concentration camps, the terror in Dachau was systematically and purposefully organized. As early as April 12, the camp leadership set an intimidating example, murdering four Jewish prisoners under the pretext that they had tried to escape.

One of the first measures undertaken was the setting up of the camp prison. Known as the "bunker", its cells consisted of a row of what had previously been double lavatories, which were fitted solely with wooden plank beds. The bunker was nothing other than a torture chamber. Of its first prisoners only the Communist Reichstag deputy Hans Beimler survived the ordeal; he was the only one who managed to escape. Under this inhumane tyranny the others were either driven to suicide or murdered.

So as to break their personality, new prisoners were subjected to severe maltreatment upon arrival in the camp. All Jews and well-known public figures, at times all new arrivals en bloc, were dealt 25 or more lashes with the bullwhip as a "welcome". The Jewish prisoners Wilhelm Aron and Louis Schloss, who arrived in Dachau on May 15, 1933, did not survive this "welcoming procedure".

Between April 12 and the end of May 1933, 13 prisoners were murdered in Dachau. Without exception these were premeditated murders ordered by the camp leadership. In no other camp were so many people killed in this period. In the other camps the state authorities exerted far greater influence than in the Dachau concentration camp, which Himmler founded as a "state camp", but which soon became the exclusive domain of the SS. The difference to the other camps located outside of Bavaria increased even more when, after the gradual disbanding of the smaller camps, the remaining prisoners were transferred to a few so-called state concentration camps, which were run by civilian managers with experience in the prison services. In Prussia these were put under the direct control of the Ministry of the Interior.

The camp regulations, formulated in 1933, bear witness to the character of the camps. Except in Dachau, these regulations express the effort to set up and run the camps on the model of normal prisons. Corporal punishment is not prescribed in any of these regulations. In stark contrast, the two

Report in the "Neue National-zeitung" on the founding of the Dachau concentration camp, March 21, 1933

sets of Dachau camp regulations document the attempt to institutionalize arbitrary tyranny and crime. These "special regulations", formulated by the camp commandant on orders from Himmler in May 1933, placed the camp under a permanent state of emergency and called for a draconian application of the death penalty. The camp commandant was vested with judicial authority. For hearing trials on incidents punishable by death, he was authorized to nominate a three- to four-member camp SS court over which he was to preside. The list of draconian punishments replaced the criminal code. The document makes no mention of defense or the possibility of submitting an appeal. The camp was to become a state within a state, furnished with its own legislature, executive, and judiciary. Only the financing was to be left to the State of Bavaria.

The May 1933 document encountered considerable resistance from within the Bavarian judicial system and government. Himmler was forced to distance himself from the conditions in Dachau and dismiss the camp commandant. But the efforts to institutionalize the rule of terror continued nonetheless. The new camp commandant Theodor Eicke elaborated a new set of regulations, known as the "disciplinary and punishment regulations", which were put into effect on October 1, 1933. This document no longer mentioned the state of emergency or the death penalty. Instead, formulations were employed such as the prisoner is to be "hanged as an agitator by virtue of revolutionary law" or "shot on the spot or subsequently hanged as a rebel". Whatever Himmler could not push through as a state official he achieved by applying "revolutionary law" in his capacity as a party functionary, as Reichsführer (imperial leader) of the SS. This perversion of the normal system was also evident in other areas in Dachau. There arose a fixed scheme for how the camp was structured and organized: the administrative system and the prisoners' self-administration. This was the origin of Eicke's notorious "school of cruelty," of disdainful flouting of the law, and of hate.

Dachau, June 28, 1938

Two different conceptions of concentration camps emerged in Germany. One, which we may call the "Prussian" variant, was geared to consolidating the regime's hold on power and was to end with the phasing out of the camp system. The other was Himmler's conception, to make the camps into instruments of terrorist intimidation and violence, by permanently suspending civil rights (based on the Reichstag Fire Emergency Decree of February 28, 1933) and utilizing Himmler's dual offices of Police Chief and Reichsführer of the SS. The combination of state power and "revolutionary" tyranny enabled limitless terror – including ideologically motivated genocide.

Himmler gradually gained control over the police in all the German states, with the exception of Prussia. In May 1934 he began to take over the Prussian concentration camps as well. Eicke was able to "distinguish" himself during the "Night of the Long Knives" on June 30, 1934. For this operation he deployed two guard units. The executions were carried out in the Dachau concentration camp, and Eicke personally shot the leader of the SA, Röhm. Eicke was then promoted to the rank of SS Gruppenführer and officially appointed Inspector of the Concentration Camps. Everywhere he annulled the existing camp regulations and introduced the draconian Dachau camp regulations and organizational system. In general, he appointed only those SS men to leading positions who had passed through his Dachau school. Of the original concentration camps there remained only Esterwegen, Lichtenburg, Moringen, Dachau and Sachsenburg, holding a total of some 4,700 protective custody prisoners. After the proclamation of Hitler's amnesty of August 7, 1934, the remaining number was only 2,394 protective custody prisoners, 1,613 of whom were detained in Dachau.

The fall in prisoner numbers was an expression of the Nazi regime's rapid consolidation of power. The political reasons for imprisonment became less important. Himmler, however, saw the concentration camps as a power and economic base for the SS. He maintained a high number of prisoners in Dachau by applying protective custody to non-political pseudo-offences, which he "politicized" by branding the "perpetrators" as pests threatening the nation, and by using empty phrases on the necessity of racial hygiene. According to the directives issued by the Bavarian Political Police, the term "pest" included beggars, hobos, gypsies, the work-shy, idlers, prostitutes, grumblers, habitual drinkers, ruffians, psychopaths, and the mentally ill.

Hitler also became interested in the prisoners as a potential labor force. By exploiting the slave labor of the prisoners, the camps were to become giant production facilities for the granite and bricks required for his monumental buildings, the so-called Führer buildings, which were to survive through the centuries as a witness to his epoch.

The low prisoner numbers in all concentration camps were only temporary. The National Socialists were preparing for war. In consultation with the Wehrmacht, they began to build the Sachsenhausen camp in 1936, shortly before constructing the camp at Buchenwald and rebuilding the Dachau concentration camp. Each of these camps had a capacity of between 6,000 and 8,000 prisoners at a time when there were a total of "only" 5,000 prisoners in protective custody in Germany. In 1937 and 1938 Himmler launched a number of arrest waves across the Reich against non-political "delinquents" and set a quota for the number of men capable of work to be placed in the concentration camps. The operations "Work-shy Reich" and the "Aso[cial] Action" filled the new concentration camps in the summer of 1938 (together with the transports of Jews from Austria). In Dachau the number of prisoners rose in the course of July from 3,410 to 6,166; 4,650 "asocial" prisoners were sent to Buchenwald and some 6,000 to Sachsenhausen. This fundamentally changed the social and political structure of the concentration camps. During the anti-Jewish pogroms throughout the Reich, the number of prisoners in Dachau rose to 14,432 in November 1938.

The Dachau concentration camp was the focus of exceptional publicity. The German daily press depicted it as a place of order and justice, while at the same time emphasizing that its prisoners were made up of abominable anthropological bastards who had to be removed from German society forever. German and foreign visitors were led through the camp so that they could convince themselves of the incorrectness of Jewish "horror propaganda". They were presented a model camp where cleanliness and order prevailed. Besides this however, they were also shown the camp's so-called anthropological museum and a group of prisoners whose appearance corresponded to the cliché of "racial inferiority".

The period of German military success, 1939-1941

Drawing by Vlastimir Kopač, March 1945

The National Socialists used the war to intensify their rule over the life and death of the prisoners. With few exceptions, releases were halted, and under the term "special treatment" the SS leadership gave itself the right to carry out executions without judicial review. This changed the composition of the prisoners, with the German prisoners soon becoming the minority. The camps became liquidation facilities. The new measures completed the prisoners' exclusion from the legal system. Besides the work performed under the yoke of terror, these measures sanctioned other features of slavery as well. The prisoners lost any right to petition for release and became a piece of property. The slave-holder organization, the SS, already long before this in charge of the prisoners' lives, was now granted the formal right to impose the death penalty. A public execution by hanging due to "work sabotage" was more threatening to the prisoners and was a more effective method of intimidation than the usual beating to death.

The National Socialists began implementing their planned Germanization and colonization of eastern Europe. From the occupied countries they deported actual and perceived potential resistance fighters and representatives of the intelligentsia

Heinrich Deubel and Oswald Pohl, administrative chief in the SS Main Office, during a camp inspection by Robert Ley, head of the German Labor Front, February 11, 1936

and public life to the concentration camps to be killed. According to the Social Darwinist notions of the National Socialists, the annihilation of leading strata of society was to negatively influence the process of natural selection, and peoples deprived of all educational opportunities would become a mindless, easy controllable mass.

The camp at Dachau was cleared at the end of September 1939 to make way for the training of frontline combat units of the SS Death's Head division; prisoners were first returned to the camp as of February 1940. During the 10 months that remained till the end of 1940, 13,375 Poles were deported to the camp, mainly from territories that were now incorporated into the German Reich as new Gaus (administrative districts). They were deported as part of the Germanization campaign based on the "blood and soil" method, which aimed at the removal of between 7 and 8 million of the native Polish population from these territories.

The consequences of this new regime in Dachau were expressed in the monstrous rise of the death rate. During the remaining 10 months of 1940, 1,521 persons lost their lives; in 1941 the number rose to 2,576. Murderous working conditions reigned above all in the large work details engaged in earth-moving and construction work. At the beginning of 1941 the "plantation" was expanded. Several hundred prisoners were driven onto a new, unfenced piece of land, called "Freiland II", where they experienced a living hell. Brutal beatings were used to make them work faster. The work they were forced to perform was often senseless. To name but one example: They were forced to cart or carry loads from one place to another until complete exhaustion. Murderous excesses were not uncommon. The Jewish prisoners, about of 200 of whom were deployed on Freiland II, were subjected to the most brutal treatment. Every day a number of dead and dying, piled into wheelbarrows, were transported away from the site at the end of the working shift.

After returning to the camp, the prisoners, hovering near death through exhaustion, were forced to stand at attention on the roll-call area for at least an hour. In the barracks new harassment, torments and draconian punishment for trifles awaited them, all imposed under the pretense of maintaining extreme cleanliness and designed to prevent exhausted prisoners from finding a moment of peace to recuperate from the daily ordeal. Given only starvation rations, the prisoners rapidly became emaciated and their psychological state deteriorated: in the six months between December 1940 and the end of May 1941, almost a quarter (23.5 per cent) of the prisoners died.

With the method of "divide and rule" the National Socialists attempted to break up the solidarity amongst the prisoners through racist and national categorizations. At the beginning, the Czech prisoners were on the bottom of the hierarchy; in the course of the war it was then the Polish, Russian, Italian and French prisoners, all of them far below the position of the German prisoners. Always at the absolute bottom rung of this hierarchy were the Jewish prisoners, however. The camp's internal administration was staffed almost exclusively by German prisoners, who were required to express their "racial superiority" with a cudgel in hand. In Dachau, where the functionary positions were in the hands of German political prisoners, conditions were not as horrific as in other camps, where criminal prisoners had the say. But even amongst the functionaries, who wore a red triangle patch, were individuals who came to relish the role of being master over the life and death of their fellow foreign and Jewish prisoners. Without their playing this sordid role, the SS would have hardly been capable of setting up such a brutal regime as existed in Dachau between 1940 and 1942.

The camp leadership demanded that the prisoner and SS personnel submit as many punishment reports as possible. One of the most frequent punishments was "pole hanging"; prisoners were hung from their hands, which were bound behind their back with chains. This punishment was imposed for a poorly made bed or a poorly cleaned locker, for not acknowledging an SS man by raising one's cap, for a chipped or unfastened button, or for having hands in one's pockets. As a rule, the wrongdoer was first brutally beaten for his "offence", before his prisoner number was then taken for report.

The so-called infirmary was a place of horror. A senior SS doctor was head of the infirmary and every ward had an SS doctor. As a rule, they were new graduates of crash-courses offered by the SS medical academy in Graz. Most of them learned surgery in the camp – more preferably on healthy, physically still robust, new prisoners, than on the emaciated, ghost-like ill (known as "bone-men"). They may have been interested in many medical issues – but least of all in curing the ill.

There were many imprisoned doctors in Dachau, but they were not permitted to work in the infirmary. This was the domain of infirmary capo Josef Heiden, a man with pathologically despotic tendencies who openly lived out his sadistic urges: he tortured to death many people whom he accused of "feigning" illness, he murdered prisoners with injections on SS orders and on his own initiative. Like the SS doctors, he learned to operate on perfectly healthy persons, and he acted as an executioner in the bunker. In the individual wards of the infirmary, head orderlies were appointed whom Heiden personally selected. The most basic equipment was lacking and there was always a pressing shortage of bandaging materials and medicines. There was no medical treatment – except for the isolated cases the SS doctors found interesting. Everything was in the hands of the orderlies, none of whom possessed the necessary medical training. Unfortunately, there were a number of disreputable individuals and primitive people amongst them, and the patients were completely at their mercy. The orderlies simply killed troublesome patients, above all those

who soiled their beds. For this purpose, beds with restraints were set up in the washroom of blocks 1 and 7. If some poor devil managed to survive the night after having cold water poured over him several times, then he was killed with an injection.

After the initial successes of the eastern campaign in 1941, a euphoria of victory overcame the National Socialists, which took on monstrous traits. Already feeling themselves to be the masters of Europe, they began to introduce their new order. As Reich Commissioner for the Strengthening of Germandom, Himmler planned extensive resettlement. The "General Plan East" outlined how the native population of the recently annexed eastern territories was to be reduced by 31 million and the rest degraded to a subhuman level of serfs without any rights. Those territories with a favorable climate were to be settled with colonists from the German Reich or people of Germanic ancestry. The system of concentration camps was to be extended on an enormous scale and millions of prisoners were to become the main labor force in realizing gigantic construction projects in the east.

This was the background to liquidating the "ballast" of those prisoners incapable of working, an operation code-named "special treatment 14 f 13": 2,674 prisoners from the Dachau concentration camp were murdered in the gas chambers of the euthanasia facility at Hartheim near Linz.

Simultaneous to reducing the Slavic population, the large-scale murdering of Soviet prisoners of war was launched. More than 3 million men of reproductive age were killed by starvation or murdered on the basis of the "commissar order". At least 4,000 Soviet prisoners of war were shot in Dachau under this pseudo-legal ruse.

The deployment of prisoners in the armaments industry, 1942 to 1945

German armaments production was geared towards achieving a lightning victory. After the defeat at Moscow and the entry of the USA into

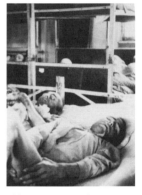

Phlegmon ward after liberation

the war in December 1941, the National Socialists were faced with having to readjust the whole economy to the demands of a long war. In February 1942 Hitler appointed Albert Speer armaments minister and commissioned Himmler with the task of placing the greatest number of prisoners possible at the disposal of the armaments industry. Himmler placed the concentration camps under the control of the SS Economic and Administration Main Office, headed by Oswald Pohl.

Working for the German war effort was to be exhausting to the point of murder, but at the same time all hindrances were to be eliminated which restricted the prisoners' capacity to work or reduced the working hours. The directives now issued to the camps collided head-on with the long-established practices and routine. The lethal working conditions were realized, but the measures benefiting the prisoners were ignored. The consequences soon became evident in the catastrophic death rate. In spite of extensive replenishment with new prisoners, the total number sank in the second half of 1942 by 10,000 and the death rate reached a monstrous monthly average of 9.9 per cent. For this reason the demands of the armaments industry could not be met in 1942.

At the end of 1942 Himmler unleashed a widespread hunt for new slaves. He set the police quotas for how many prisoners capable of work were to be deported to the concentration camps, and he exploited all kinds of incidents for collective reprisals and raids. Transports arrived at the concentration camps with residents from depopulated partisan areas and later from areas evacuated because of the advancing combat front.
The death rate only began to drop as Pohl replaced the camp commandants and Himmler allowed the prisoners to receive food packages. While the living conditions of the working prisoners improved, those incapable of work were mercilessly eliminated. The prisoners capable of work were to also be annihilated as before, only now this was to

be realized in a way productive for the Reich: they were to be worked to death. This method was called "extermination through work".

After overcoming the phase of stagnation, the number of prisoners in the concentration camp system rose rapidly. From 88,000 in December 1942, it increased to 224,000 by August 1943, and by August the following year it had doubled again to 534,000, before reaching between 714,000 and 750,000 in January 1945.

Due to Allied air superiority the losses suffered by the German armaments industry grew. In response, the "Jäger program" was launched in March 1944. The goal was to transfer the production of jet fighters underground. The largest project was the construction of six gigantic bunkers with a monthly production capacity of 3,000 planes. The rapid developments on the warfront meant, however, that work was ultimately limited to construction work on two of these bunkers near Landsberg-Kaufering (40 miles to the west) and Mühldorf (70 miles east). The subcamps to Dachau were set up in their vicinity, the Kaufering and Mühldorf complexes with Jewish prisoners. Shelter was primitive, most of them were mere dugouts covered with grass, offering hardly any protection against the cold and damp. The heavy labor and insufficient rations caused a rapid deterioration of the prisoners' physical state; those who could no longer work were sent to the gas chambers at Auschwitz.

We now come to the tragic final phase. In historical studies we often encounter the tendency to explain the horrors of this last phase as the result of chaotic conditions. When we analyze the sources in a broader context however, the contours of a monstrous, intentionally implemented crime emerge.

As early as July 20, 1944, the prisons and collection camps of the Gestapo in the General Government of Poland had received the order to liquidate all those prisoners and Jews who could not be removed in time from the advancing front. The evacuation transports were murderous from the very beginning. However, the order that no prisoner was to fall into the hands of the enemy alive could not be implemented completely. Left behind in the camps were sick persons and those unable to march whom the Nazis had not managed to murder in time. The National Socialists thus began their murder operations earlier in the remaining camps. Beginning in February 1945, thousands of prisoners unable to walk were murdered with gas or other means; thousands of others were sent to Bergen-Belsen where a terrible typhus epidemic performed the same function as the gas chambers. At the same time, Himmler sought to establish contact with the Allies through representatives of the International Red Cross, promising to spare the lives of some groups of prisoners if certain political conditions were met.

On April 18, as the danger loomed of Germany being split into a north-south divide by the advancing fronts, Himmler decided that the prisoners in the remaining concentration camps of northern Germany were to be evacuated via the Baltic Sea, where they were obviously supposed to drown. The prisoners from the southern part of Germany were to be concentrated in the Alps region, from where Himmler intended to form a resistance front against the Allies with his SS. At the same time, he issued the order that no prisoner was to fall into enemy hands alive.

The transports from Neuengamme (near Hamburg) and some northern subcamps of Dora-Mittelbau were routed to the area of Lübeck Bay. From Stutthof (near Gdansk), around 3,000 ill prisoners who were not evacuated were also transported to the area in canal barges. Overcrowded with prisoners, the ships Cap Arcona and Thielbeck set off for the open sea, where they were mistakenly bombed by British planes and sank. The evacuation columns from Sachsenhausen and Ravensbrück were liberated chiefly by Soviet troops and, on occasion, by US forces.

In Dachau the situation had worsened dramatically. The camp was hopelessly overcrowded, the hygienic conditions became disastrous, and the food rations were insufficient to live on. In November 1944 a typhus epidemic had raged, spreading rapidly and feeding on the incessant stream of emaciated people who had survived the death transports from the evacuated camps. The subcamp complexes of Kaufering and Mühldorf were also severely affected. In November 1944 997 prisoners died, in December 1,915, and in the first three months of 1945 10,427 prisoners lost their lives.

In contrast to the other concentration camps, in Dachau those prisoners unable to walk were not murdered, although the camp did have a gas chamber. The difficulties involved in removing the thousands of corpses certainly played a role in this regard. The capacity of the crematorium was insufficient, and as coal supplies ran out in February it was shut down completely. The camp leadership buried the dead in mass graves on the nearby Leitenberg hill.

It is likely that those prisoners unable to walk were not murdered because there was no plan to evacuate the main Dachau camp or the Jewish subcamps. The chief of the SS Main Office of Reich Security, Kaltenbrunner, was later accused at the Nuremberg Trials of ordering the death of the camp's prisoners through aerial bombing and poisoned rations. When it became untenable to execute this plan due to the chaotic conditions and the unwillingness of the relevant functionaries, it was decided to evacuate the camp after all. Without any consideration for the dangers posed to the local population, 10,000 prisoners from the typhus-infected camp were marched off in the direction of the Alps on April 26.

In the final phase resistance groups based on nationality were formed. They wanted to resist the imminent threat of mass elimination by the SS. On April 28, a group of escaped prisoners organized an armed uprising in the town of Dachau, but it

Eastern section of the bunker construction site "Weingut I", Mühldorf, 1945

was bloodily crushed by the superior forces of the SS within a few hours. During the following night an international prisoners' committee was formed in the camp, and on the next day the camp was liberated by units belonging to the 42nd and 45th infantry divisions of the 7th US Army.

Barbara Distel
The Dachau Concentration Camp after Liberation

With the opening of the new main exhibition on the history of the Dachau concentration camp on May 2, 2003, located in the rooms of the former maintenance building, the new lay-out of the Dachau Memorial Site reached its initial conclusion, 70 years after the original concentration camp was set up. Working together with survivors of the concentration camp, in 1995-1996 an expert advisory board, appointed by the Bavarian Minister of Education and Cultural Affairs, had elaborated a conception for a large new main exhibition and several smaller exhibitions to replace the previous exhibition from 1965. Furthermore, the conception increased the information resources on the grounds and relocated the visitors' entrance from the east to to the west side, so that visitors would enter through the original gate of the former concentration camp. The House of Bavarian History in Augsburg was assigned responsibility for coordinating the realization of the new conception. Along with the ongoing contributions by concentration camp survivors and representatives from the Dachau Memorial Site and the Bavarian Office for Civic Education, an advisory board of experts accompanied the realization process for the full seven years.

The official opening of the new comprehensive exhibition – 70 years after the Dachau concentration camp was established and 58 years after US Army units liberated the survivors – marked an important new period for the Memorial Site. The postwar history of the site had increasingly attracted the interest of both the general public and historical research in the preceding years: how the responsible authorities dealt with the camp grounds after liberation, how the grounds were used for a variety of purposes, and how the survivors attempted to have a memorial site created there. When the decision was reached to realize a new exhibition in 1995, the Memorial Site already looked back on thirty years of existence. At that point in time, the sites of remembrance on the former concentration camp grounds had already existed more than twice as long as the camp itself.

The chronology of the site after the dramatic hours when over 30,000 concentration camp prisoners who had survived their ordeal were liberated by US Army units on April 29, 1945 can be divided into four different phases, each of varying duration.

1. Between liberation and beginning a new life

News of the catastrophic conditions that the American liberators found in the Dachau concentration camp on April 29, 1945, filmed by US war reporters and the subject of press reports, was sent around the world. The name of Dachau subsequently became a synonym for crimes against humanity. It took three months, until the end of July 1945, before the last survivors were able to leave the camp grounds. In this period, the American liberators were confronted with enormous problems: the dead had to be buried, the ill cared for, and the hungry provided for. The camp had to be placed immediately under quarantine due to a rampant typhus epidemic, which cost several thousand prisoners their lives even after liberation. To contain the danger of contagion, it was absolutely necessary to improve the catastrophic sanitary conditions in the overcrowded barracks. Together with representatives from the individual nations, who had joined together to form an international committee, the Americans organized this transition from complete chaos to reasonably ordered civilian life and prepared the repatriation of the survivors. Most Jewish survivors, whose families had been murdered and property and possessions stolen, did not want to return to their native countries, above all those in eastern Europe. They were placed in so-called displaced persons camps. After the SS guards had fled, Allied soldiers had taken charge of a great majority of the survivors from the subcamps at a variety of places along the routes of the death marches. Most of the subcamps had been evacuated a few days before liberation, and the prisoners driven southward by SS guards. The liberated prisoners were taken to hospitals in the near vicinity or

Aerial photo of the Memorial Site, around 1969

housed in other buildings. In Dachau, an International Information Office was set up, where survivors used the remaining preserved documents and file cards to attempt to determine and document the fate of the more than 200,000 prisoners who had been in the Dachau camp.

2. Internment and American military court proceedings, 1945 to 1948

In July 1945, both the former prisoner camp and the SS camp grounds were converted into an internment camp administered by the American military. Initially, around 25,000 persons were committed and placed in different sections of the camp. These persons were divided into the following groups:

– Members of the SS and functionaries of the Nazi party and its affiliated organizations who were covered by the category of "automatic arrest": they formed the largest group initially. The first of these prisoners were released at the beginning of 1946.

– Officers of the Wehrmacht (German army) who were being held in a sectioned-off POW camp located in the former SS camp. The first releases here took place in 1946 as well; this camp was disbanded in 1947.

– From these two groups persons were selected who were suspected of involvement in war crimes and crimes against humanity. They were placed in a War Crimes Enclosure (closed-off area for suspected war criminals), where they either waited for trial or for extradition to other countries.

– Finally, in 1947, a transition camp was set up for civilian internees against whom no involvement in crimes could be proven. They went through the so-called denazification proceedings, under the auspices of German arbitration courts. These courts were disbanded in 1948.

The first major military trial in Dachau began on November 15, 1945, with 40 defendants facing charges based on crimes committed in the Dachau concentration camp. This trial became a model for those to follow ("parent case"). Upon its conclusion, 36 defendants were sentenced to death, 28 of whom were later executed in Landsberg prison. Further trials followed, dealing not only with other crimes committed in the Dachau concentration camp and its subcamps, but also in the concentration camps of Mauthausen, Flossenbürg, Mühldorf, Mittelbau-Dora, and Buchenwald. In addition to these crimes committed in concentration camps, trials were heard against members of the SS who had perpetrated crimes against Allied soldiers. Overall, 1,672 accused were brought to trial in 489 proceedings before American military courts. Death sentences were passed in 426 cases, although not all of these were then carried out, and there were 256 acquittals. At the beginning of the 1950s, as the policy of the Western Allies changed during the Cold War, prison sentences were reduced or waived.

3. The refugee camp and the struggle for establishing a memorial site, 1948 to 1965

In January 1948, the US authorities handed over the former prisoner camp to the Bavarian state government. The entire area of the SS camp as well as the entrance building, the camp prison and a wing of the maintenance building remained, however, under the control of the American military administration for 25 more years. The Bavarian authorities immediately arranged for refugees and homeless people to be accommodated in the barracks camp, which was first called the "former internment camp" and then officially the "Dachau East residential settlement". The settlement was developed considerably in the following decade. Industry, businesses, restaurants and bars, cinemas, a school and a kindergarten were all built. The water and power systems were repaired and renewed. With the exception of the adjacent crematorium area, which was surrounded by a wall and cared for as a memorial site always open to the public, nothing remained that refered to the site's history as a concentration camp. In these years there was essentially no

American military court, Dachau 1945-46

public interest in the history of the years between 1933 and 1945 and the fate of the victims of the National Socialist dictatorship in the vicinity of Dachau. The 1955 demand by Dachau's representative in the Bavarian State Parliament that the crematorium be torn down in order to put an end to the "defamation of the Dachau area" was not the only attempt to remove the architectural remnants of the concentration camp. French concentration camp survivors protested against the removal of an earlier exhibition in 1953, and the demolition of the guard towers, which began in 1957, was stopped by a local survivor. A supplementary agreement to the Paris Treaties, signed by the West German government in September 1955, mandated the preservation and care of graves of victims of the Nazi regime, explicitly including Dachau. This at least ensured the continuing existence of the crematorium area as a memorial site. Responsibility for this area had already been transferred to the Bavarian Heritage Office in 1952.

From about 1948 onwards, the Cold War increasingly hindered ties between survivors in eastern and western Europe, ultimately making communication virtually impossible. In Germany as well, the former victims of persecution organized themselves anew according to their respective political leanings. In this context, the re-founding of an International Committee for the survivors of the Dachau concentration camp, which had already existed in secret in the final phase before liberation, was the first important step on the difficult path to establishing a memorial site that would conserve and pass on the legacy of all prisoners. The first task was to win over allies who could convince politicians and the public of the significance of this project. Beginning in 1959, a Bavarian board of trustees composed of representatives from public institutions and associations, the greater majority of whom were surviving victims of persecution, actively campaigned on the side of the International Prisoners' Committee for establishing a memorial site. In 1960 a Catholic chapel was built on the concentration camp grounds, on the joint initiative of concentration camp survivors and Munich bishop Johannes Neuhäusler. When 50,000 participants from around the world attended its dedication during the Eucharistic World Congress in June, it was obvious that any continued neglect of this site of European history would no longer be acceptable. At first, in the same year, survivors presented a documentary exhibition in the rooms of the large crematorium. Next, in 1962, the Bavarian state government and the Comité International de Dachau signed an agreement of intent to create a memorial site on the grounds of the former prisoner camp, with a large documentary exhibition in the former maintenance building. The barracks, which were either greatly altered after 1945 or had become dilapidated, were torn down after the last residents of the refugee camp had left. The first two barracks were reconstructed and the walls and guard towers repaired. As the original entrance building continued to remain in the hands of the American military administration, a provisional entrance was built in the eastern outer wall.

On May 9, 1965, on the twentieth anniversary of the concentration camp's liberation, the memorial site and the new documentary exhibition were opened, with a large number of survivors from almost all countries of Europe in attendance. In 1967 two further religious buildings were erected on the grounds of the former prisoner camp, a Protestant Church of Reconciliation and a Jewish memorial. The project initiated by the Dachau concentration camp survivors was brought to a conclusion with the unveiling of the memorial on the former roll-call area in 1968. The International Dachau Commitee had staged an international competition that was won by the Jewish sculptor Nandor Glid from Belgrade. In hindsight we have to acknowledge that the design of the 1960s Dachau Memorial Site mirrored the views and interests of the surviving prisoners. Without their initiative and persistence the project never would have been realized. The emphasis on the religious buildings erected in the Memorial Site, which was

Guard tower of the former concentration camp,

due to bishop Johannes Neuhäusler's ability to assert his views, is an indication of this. The first section of the 1965 documentary exhibition, which covers the formative history of the Third Reich, insisted on by the German survivors, is another. Personal biographies and the history of persecution suffered by individuals were, in contrast, not taken up as themes; indeed, giving prominence to individual fates was consciously avoided. It was the survivors' conviction that the Dachau Memorial Site was to be a collective memorial and testimony, one that should serve the commemoration of the victims and the education of following generations. Facts, data and documents dispersed across the whole world connected with the history of the concentration camp were collected and brought to Dachau with the assistance of the survivors.

4. The memorial site of the former Dachau concentration camp, 1965 to 1995. Three decades of fostering remembrance

The crimes committed on the various groups of prisoners continued to dominate during the first decade after the opening of the memorial site in 1965, a decade that was shaped by the active participation of persons personally affected by this history. Some 300,000 visitors came to the memorial site every year, the overwhelming majority – up to 75 per cent in some years – from abroad. The proportion of survivors and their relatives was still very high, the interest shown by the German public in contrast very low. Only a few school classes and youth groups visited the Memorial Site, even though in 1964 the Bavarian Ministry of Education and Cultural Affairs had issued a recommendation for graduating classes at Bavarian schools to visit a concentration camp memorial site located in Bavaria. Didactic conceptions and civic education ideas did not yet play a role in this period.

The situation at the Dachau memorial site changed fundamentally between 1975 and 1985. This decade was characterized by a continuing dramatic rise in the annual number of visitors, yielding ultimately a threefold increase. With 900,000 visitors it eventually even approached the one million mark. At the same time, worldwide interest in the history of Nazi crimes against humanity was developing, and new memorial sites and research centers were established in many countries. In Dachau, the number of German school classes and youth groups now increased disproportionately, the share of German visitors rising to almost 50 per cent of the total number. The same period also saw a greater interest in the life stories of the survivors. Teachers and pedagogues involved in youth and adult education increasingly turned to eyewitnesses. The Dachau Memorial Site, at the time one of the few places where the voices of the surviving victims were given a platform and listened to, became a location for intergenerational encounters and for informing first hand about the fates of the prisoners. New historical questions, such as the fate of the hitherto "forgotten victims" of the Nazi dictatorship, such as Sinti and Roma, Jehovah's Witnesses and homosexuals, attracted more attention. As in many other places initiatives were launched for researching local history between 1933 and 1945. The significance of the subcamps, set up in the final phase of the camp's history, became increasingly clear. In the 1980s, four decades after liberation, those Jewish survivors who had been sent to the Dachau subcamps towards the end of the war and who immigrated to Israel after liberation, were for the first time willing to return and enter into dialogue with young Germans.

The political changes triggered by the year 1989 also had an impact on the Dachau Memorial Site. In connection with a broad discussion on new conceptions for the concentration camp memorial sites located in the former East Germany, West Germany's responsibility for all memorial sites of National Socialist terror became an issue for the first time. As a result, the federal government contributed to meeting the costs for realizing the new Dachau Memorial Site.

The former prisoner Adi Maislinger with a youth group in the Dachau Memorial Site, 1970s

After the iron curtain fell, the remaining survivors who had lived behind it now began to make their presence felt in the West. Most of the survivors in the countries of the former Soviet Union had been deported to Germany as children or youths. After their return to the Soviet Union from the German camps in 1945, many were once more arrested, detained in camps, and subjected to forced labor. In old age most of them lived in bitter poverty and without adequate medical care. In the 1990s, they addressed their hopes for assistance and compensation for the suffering inflicted on them to the Federal Republic of Germany and, in many cases, directly to the memorial sites. At the same time, the survivors began to retrace the steps of their own personal history of persecution, which had been submerged for half a century. In addition to the foundation set up in 2000 by the German federal government and industrial companies for compensating victims of forced labor in the Nazi state, which was to financially assist survivors chiefly from eastern Europe, the Dachau Memorial Site also became a contact point for hundreds of potential claimants.

The annual number of visitors to the Dachau Memorial Site from all over the globe has remained consistently high. They are mainly young people who come to the "learning and remembrance site Dachau" in the course of history or civic education programs. The necessity of providing more nuanced didactic conceptions grows stronger as the number of historical witnesses decreases. "However," said a young theologian in 1998, "the fate of memory does not depend on the size of video and other archives, nor on the capacity of digital media, but rather on the courage and convictions of those who were touched by the message of the witnesses and who continue to inhabit this world."

The "Death March" monument, Hubertus von Pilgrim, 1990

Wolfgang Benz
Places of Remembrance, Culture of Remembrance

History is made up of collective memories, and often of bitter experiences as well, such as those during the era of National Socialist rule, when anti-Semitism was a state doctrine and the persecution of minorities escalated into genocide. The desecrated and destroyed synagogues, for which there are no Jewish communities any more, are symbols of this past. The experience of persecution is not limited to one minority, however. Other persecuted ethnic, social and religious groups, such as the Sinti and Roma, homosexuals, "asocial elements" and Jehovah's Witnesses, remained stigmatized beyond the collapse of National Socialism, forgotten, and neither acknowledged nor respected as victims. Considerable sections of the majority society were also discriminated against, repressed or persecuted if they risked participating in the struggle between the Nazi state and the churches, in the labor movement, or opposed the regime in other ways. Remembering their perseverance and unwavering resistance was a highly political issue that was politically exploited after 1945, in different ways depending on which of the two postwar German states recognized that historical experience.

The "Death March" monument, Hubertus von Pilgrim

For individuals as well as for the society in which they live, remembering is an element of self-reflection, an element of identity, and, like forgetting, necessary for all human existence. Remembering forges self-confidence and peace, but remembering also torments and is painful. Symbols and rituals are helpful in forging meaning out of remembering for both contemporaries and subsequent generations, and in making remembrance public. Individual remembering broadens out into public, collective memory, becoming a part of political culture, given expression on days like November 9 and January 27, which are devoted to the memory of a past that weighs heavily, and finding expression in artistically rendered signs, in monuments at important sites, which then also become places for ceremonies and official signals, for state occasions and public acts of commemoration.

But nowhere does memory crystallize with a more powerful and oppressive force than at those historical sites and places where the events shaping this very remembrance and determining memory occurred: the authentic sites of history. In Dachau one of first institutions for suppressing criticism and resistance against National Socialism was erected, and Dachau was the concentration camp that became the model for the persecution apparatus and the model and training center for the "order of terror" in the National Socialist state. As a memorial site, as a place of learning, as a source of information with its exhibitions and presentation of authentic remnants, Dachau thus has an extraordinarily important position in the landscape of German remembrance and memory.

Historical memory and the consensus about it, even if they are based on the results of research and analysis, on credible sources and eyewitness accounts, are not simply givens in terms of their content; they must be constantly defined anew and defended. This is because history is not a dead past, but a challenge that palpably reaches into our present. The discussions about monuments and memorial sites, about protecting historical buildings, the debates about compensation for the victims of National Socialism, about the overdue payments for former forced laborers, the instances of violence perpetrated by right wing extremists – all these are proof of the continuing effects of the National Socialist legacy.

For some time now, indeed for years, discussion has focused on monuments, on artistically rendered memorials that shall hold the crimes of National Socialism in everyone's memory. In memory? Or is it a matter of "commemoration", of rituals and ceremonies, of relocating collective memory onto a meta-level, onto the field where the array of feelings we term "emotional impact" (Betroffenheit) flourish, possibly even into an esoteric realm?

A former synagogue as a restored building harbors quite a few dangers for remembrance. A restored synagogue is a fragment of a recreated unscathed world that makes us forget the intrusion of barbarism. A reconstructed synagogue in which no rabbi prays with the faithful and no cantor sings, because there are no more Jews there, could become an idyllic cultural haven that portrays only one part of historical reality: its better aspect. A restored synagogue used as a concert hall for Klezmer music and for cultural performances, but without reference to its original function, a synagogue as an auditorium or a place for staging the routine experience of gestures of emotional affect, represents an attempt to remember that is just as misguided as visiting a war museum in the hope of learning pacifist convictions there.

In contrast to the lively discussion about the Berlin central Holocaust monument, the memorial sites on authentic sites, on the grounds of concentration camps, in the ghettos, the places of torture or the execution pits have very much remained on the margins of public attention. Of course the idea of a generously outfitted memorial building or monument at a central location is far more attractive than the loneliness and gloomy bleakness of former concentration camps, where the suffering of the victims is still palpable decades later. A museum, a library, a monumental artwork – there are many aspects that seem more attractive than an authentic site with its mute challenge to think, to face up to the burden of history.

Remembering needs, however, places saturated with the aura of the what happened that can serve as points where understanding can crystallize, and it needs memorial sites, which, furthermore, offer explanations that make individual learning through rational comprehension possible. Of course such memorial sites must also be embedded in a context where citizens feel responsible for them, and are willing to further the cause of institutionalized remembrance and thereby turn them into places that are alive with engagement with history. This is also necessary so that memorial sites can lose the character of places shrouded in taboos.

The landscape of historical sites, as the topography of remembering, repressing, and forgetting, has many aspects, including some lesser-known ones. This includes buildings which – changed or unchanged – are still in use, for example in Berlin: the centrally located airport in Tempelhof, the Olympic stadium, or the Reich Ministry of Aviation – Göring's ministry. Under Soviet occupation the latter housed the German Economic Commission, the precursor of the East German government, and then served as the "House of Ministries" in East Germany, before the Federal Trust Agency moved in after the fall of the Berlin wall to reverse the socialization of industry and privatize formerly state-owned companies. After a few years, the Trust Agency made way for the current tenant, the Federal Ministry of Finance. Other relics without reference to their origin are the streetlamps in Berlin designed by Albert Speer, the autobahn maintenance centers and youth hostels in the "Heimat" (homeland) style spread across Germany, the remnants of the "Gau" (Nazi administrative district) forums and the "Ordensburgen" (castle-like complexes serving as Nazi elite schools), the residential settlements for members of the SS and other party organizations, and the everyday buildings that served the Nazis as tools for exercising control over the population and where today nothing recalls their former function. A range of sites are subsumed under the enigmatic term "war grave sites", including German military cemeteries and the special camps of the Soviet secret police NKVD in the former Soviet zone of occupation, local sites of terror where victims are buried, or which subsume other direct or indirect remnants of the National Socialist era.

Berlin Tempelhof

Common to these relics is that visitors are often unable to find out anything about the origin, the initial function and the significance of the site. The "House of Art" in Munich betrays its origins more clearly than the former "Gau" Aviation Command Center in Prinzregentenstrasse, currently home to the Bavarian Economics Ministry, or, to name another example of Nazi architecture in Munich, the building in the Ludwigstrasse now serving the Ministry of Agriculture, in which the National Socialist "Gauleiter" of Upper Bavaria once resided. The Königsplatz in Munich, designed in the 19th century by Leo von Klenze for Ludwig I as a homage to antiquity, was degraded and turned into a central place for glorifying the military by the National Socialists. For Nazi oath of allegiance ceremonies, held at night to heighten their effect, like the annual SS parade on November 9, this area was covered with special slabs that amplified the stomping sound made by the boots of the military formations as they marched across the square.

Today there is nothing that recalls this use of the square, which in 1988 was restored to its original state and is now seen solely as a noble ensemble typical of nineteenth-century artistic city planning. The two monumental buildings bordering the square on its eastern end, built between 1934 and 1939 as the head administrative office of the Nazi Party and as a headquarters for the Führer, are now used by a music college and various research institutes, and nothing whatsoever points out that here the Munich Agreement, which sacrificed Czechoslovakia to pacify Hitler, was drafted and publicly announced. Between the Führer headquarters and the administrative building a biotope has flourished on the remaining foundations of two "temples of honor", whose superstructures were demolished in 1947, where the Nazis had annually commemorated those who had "fallen" in the Hitler Putsch of 1923. How this natural enclave has come about in the middle of a large city remains a mystery to uninformed visitors. Of course, these kinds of remnants are not suitable for staging commemorations. But on-site information about the key importance this square and its surroundings possessed for National Socialism, which as a movement defined itself precisely through cultic worship at such sites, would be necessary as an explanation of how the idea of a "Volk community" was exploited.

Königsplatz, Munich

Memorial sites located on the grounds of former concentration camps are the most prominent anchors of memory, and they are officially established in political culture. Since the 1960s they are places where ceremonies are held, official state visits led to, and which school pupils and interested citizens visit. Known in East Germany as "national sites of warning and commemoration", in West Germany no national claim was raised, and the grounds are simply called concentration camp memorial sites. As the focal points of National Socialist rule, the concentration camps were ubiquitous. Almost every community of even modest size in the German Reich, and later in the German occupied territories as well, had a concentration camp or at least some form of branch camp. After the initial phase of spontaneous proliferation, the subsequent rise and extension of the terror system followed calculated plans and was painstakingly organized down to the smallest detail. The larger concentration camps were first turned into memorial sites in the 1960s. Many of the subcamps however have simply been forgotten, while others are present in contemporary consciousness thanks to the care and activism of concernd local residents and, in some cases, municipal authorities. Nevertheless, there is a widespread tendency to play down the existence of a local concentration camp (or one of its subcamps). This was not a concentration camp but only a "work camp" is an argument brought forth for many years now, glossing over the historical reality and soothing the collective conscience. To maintain the everyday presence of the Nazi regime in public memory, memorial sites on historical sites are more important than centrally organized and staged acts of commemoration. Based on a concretization of historical events, the memorial sites serve to provide both rational and emotional assistance in recognizing and understanding the inner mechanics of National Socialist tyranny, of how it evinced consent if not approval, of its persecution practices, and of the resistance against the regime. The enormous visitor numbers at some sites (Dachau for instance has some 700,000 annually) should not deceive us into believing that the memorial sites are places of general public interest. School classes for instance are encouraged to visit the memorial sites for pedagogical reasons, foreign visitors come for a diverse array of reasons (including to confirm resentments), so that the main body of visitors are persons with special motivations. Normal citizens view memorial sites more as stigmatized places, at best as necessary ceremonial sites, which they will not visit voluntarily if they can avoid it. We must also ask how the aversion of memorial sites can be overcome and how they can be integrated into the discourse of public remembrance, where they must assume a central role.

Public remembrance is necessary for creating meaning in political culture, and it requires specific forms of ritual and concretization. Of course the risk remains that monumentalizing and ritualizing the events will promote the pathos of brief emotional catharsis more than it will foster thoughtful and considered recollection, so that participants experience the general emotional outpouring as an isolated event, after which, reassured once more, they can carry on as usual. Instead of a fleeting surge of remembrance on anniversary dates, instead of centralized, stylized, media-appropriate commemoration, efforts must be undertaken to incorporate remembrance into everyday public consciousness: ceremonious evocations and soothing pronouncements without any individual remembering are more likely to remain ineffective in the long run. Public staging is no substitute for private engagement and reflection. And for that, memorial sites in particular are necessary: authentic sites where historical events become vivid and concrete, where it is possible to comprehend, at least to a certain extent, what happened.

Remembering will continue to be necessary in the future: remembering the era of National Socialism, remembering the Holocaust, in a time soon to come in which there will no longer be any eye-witnesses, any survivors of the persecution. For this we in Germany need memorial sites on authentic sites.

Memorial sites are necessary, but they cannot exist in a vacuum. They have to be interwoven with the everyday work of remembrance, they must be places of dialogue, and they need the support and commitment of citizens and politicians.

Remembrance is not performed however by simply delegating it to memorial sites, to monuments and museums, to archives and libraries, or to research institutes. And memorial sites must avoid petrifying into cult-like places of emotion. The memorial sites on the grounds of former concentration camps and other locations of National Socialist crimes are places of learning that serve to create meaning for the political culture of a democratic state.

The Jourhaus

Memorial sites are key places of engagement with and reflection on history, they are places of cultural experience; but it is not enough to manifest the remembrance of National Socialism solely at the more prominent sites and central locations. Remembrance must – calmly and assuredly – be a component in the everyday political culture of the country.

Memorial sites must therefore be integrated into the general public culture of remembrance; they must, for example, become sites for important political announcements, and not just enter the public stage on the anniversary of liberation or during the visits of foreign dignitaries.

At the same time, we have to warn about false expectations. Memorial sites cannot compensate for deficiencies in the education system, nor can they instantly prevent or reverse developments triggered by social frustration, for instance adolescent violence or extremist right wing thinking. Memorial sites are not repair shops for fixing what is going wrong in society. They can only provide issues to think about, based on and conveyed by examining closely what remains of the past. Those issues then have to be pursued elsewhere.

The historical site at Dachau is part of the nation's heritage, and as the place where the collapse of civilized culture began, it has a significance that surpasses local and national remembrance. The Dachau Concentration Camp Memorial Site is a component of our political culture – as a location for self-reflection, as a place of learning, as a place enabling personal encounters, and certainly not the least, as a place that can help to bring about peace.

Chronology of the Dachau Concentration Camp, 1933-1945

Chronology of the Dachau Concentration Camp, 1933-1945

	The Dachau Concentration Camp	The German Reich
1933	Opening of a concentration camp for political prisoners near Dachau (March 22, 1933)	Adolf Hitler becomes Reich Chancellor; establishment of the National Socialist dictatorship
1934	Murder of 21 NSDAP functionaries and political opponents arrested during the "Röhm Putsch"	"Röhm Putsch" – the rise of the SS
1935	Delivery of new prisoners, for example Jehovah's Witnesses, homosexuals, emigrants	The Nuremberg Laws institutionalizing racial discrimination
1936	Terror in the camp is intensified	Heinrich Himmler becomes German Police Chief; the creation of a concentration camp system begins
1937	At the beginning of the year construction of a new camp with a capacity for 6,000 prisoners starts	During mass arrests thousands are taken into "preventive custody" and sent to concentration camps
1938	Committal of political opponents from the "annexed" territories as well as over 11,000 German and Austrian Jews in November	"Annexation" of Austria and the Sudetenland; the November pogrom ("Night of Broken Glass")
1939	Deportation of hundreds of Sinti and Roma to the Dachau concentration camp	Attack on Poland; begin of the Second World War
1940	Over 13,000 prisoners are sent from Poland	After the capitulation of France, French, Dutch, Belgian territory has been occupied and Luxemburg annexed
1941	Start of the mass execution of over 4,000 Soviet prisoners of war	Attack on the Soviet Union
1942	"Invalid transports" – more than 2,500 prisoners are murdered by poison gas at Hartheim castle near Linz	"Wannsee Conference" on the "final solution of the Jewish question"
1943	Construction of over 150 subcamps begins, where the prisoners have to perform forced labor for the armaments industry	"Total war": radicalization of forced labor to ensure the "final victory"
1944	10,000 Jewish prisoners are killed in the subcamps "through work". At the end of 1944 there are over 63,000 prisoners in the Dachau concentration camp and its subcamps: the catastrophic living conditions lead to an outbreak of typhus	The Western Allies land in Normandy, Russian troops reach the eastern border of Germany
1945	Thousands die of typhus, in the course of evacuation marches or as a consequence of malnutrition. Founding of an international prisoner committee (CID). Liberation of the camp by U.S. Army troops (April 29, 1945)	Unconditional surrender (May 8, 1945), occupation and division of Germany

The Dachau Concentration Camp with Subcamps (detail)

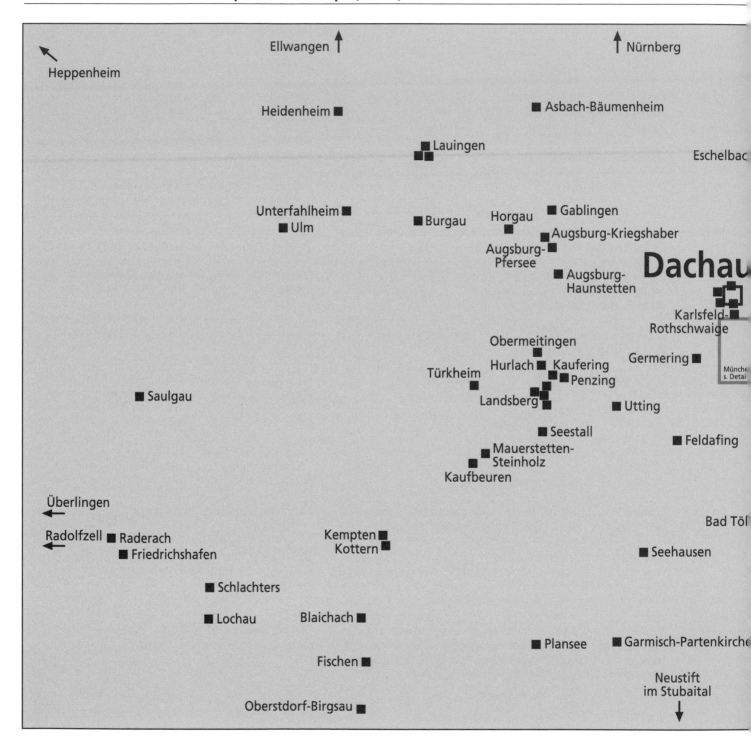

Heppenheim ↖

Ellwangen ↑

Nürnberg ↑

■ Heidenheim

■ Asbach-Bäumenheim

■ ■ Lauingen

Eschelbac

■ Unterfahlheim

■ Burgau

Horgau ■

■ Gablingen

Augsburg-Kriegshaber ■

Augsburg-Pfersee ■

Dachau

■ Augsburg-Haunstetten

Karlsfeld-Rothschwaige ■

Obermeitingen ■

Germering ■

München s. Detai

Hurlach ■ ■ Kaufering

Türkheim ■

■ ■ Penzing

Saulgau ■

Landsberg ■ ■

■ Utting

■ Seestall

■ Feldafing

■ Mauerstetten-Steinholz

■ Kaufbeuren

Überlingen ←

Bad Töl

Radolfzell ← ■ Raderach

Kempten ■

■ Seehausen

■ Friedrichshafen

Kottern ■

■ Schlachters

■ Lochau

Blaichach ■

■ Plansee

■ Garmisch-Partenkirche

Fischen ■

Neustift im Stubaital ↓

Oberstdorf-Birgsau ■

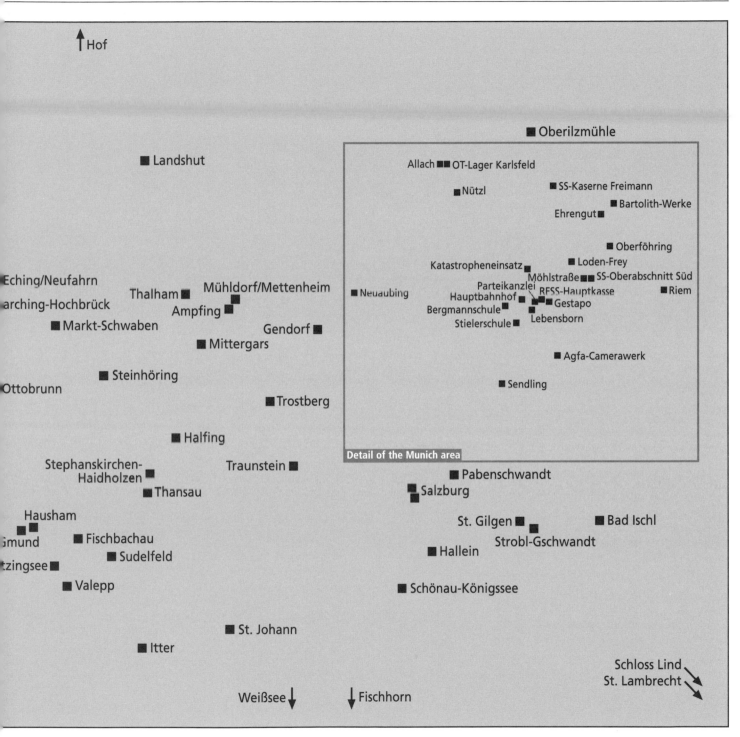

↑ Hof

■ Landshut

■ Oberilzmühle

Allach ■■ OT-Lager Karlsfeld

■ Nützl

■ SS-Kaserne Freimann

Ehrengut ■

■ Bartolith-Werke

■ Oberföhring

Katastropheneinsatz ■

■ Loden-Frey

Möhlstraße ■■ SS-Oberabschnitt Süd

Parteikanzlei

Eching/Neufahrn

Thalham ■

Mühldorf/Mettenheim

■ Neuaubing

Hauptbahnhof

RFSS-Hauptkasse

■ Riem

arching-Hochbrück

Ampfing ■

Bergmannschule ■

■ Gestapo

■ Markt-Schwaben

Gendorf ■

Stielerschule ■

Lebensborn

■ Mittergars

Ottobrunn

■ Steinhöring

■ Agfa-Camerawerk

■ Sendling

■ Trostberg

■ Halfing

Detail of the Munich area

Stephanskirchen-
Haidholzen ■

Traunstein ■

■ Pabenschwandt

■ Salzburg

■ Thansau

Hausham

St. Gilgen ■

■ Bad Ischl

Gmund ■

■ Fischbachau

Strobl-Gschwandt

zingsee ■

■ Sudelfeld

■ Hallein

■ Valepp

■ Schönau-Königssee

■ St. Johann

■ Itter

Schloss Lind ↘

St. Lambrecht ↘

Weißsee ↓

↓ Fischhorn

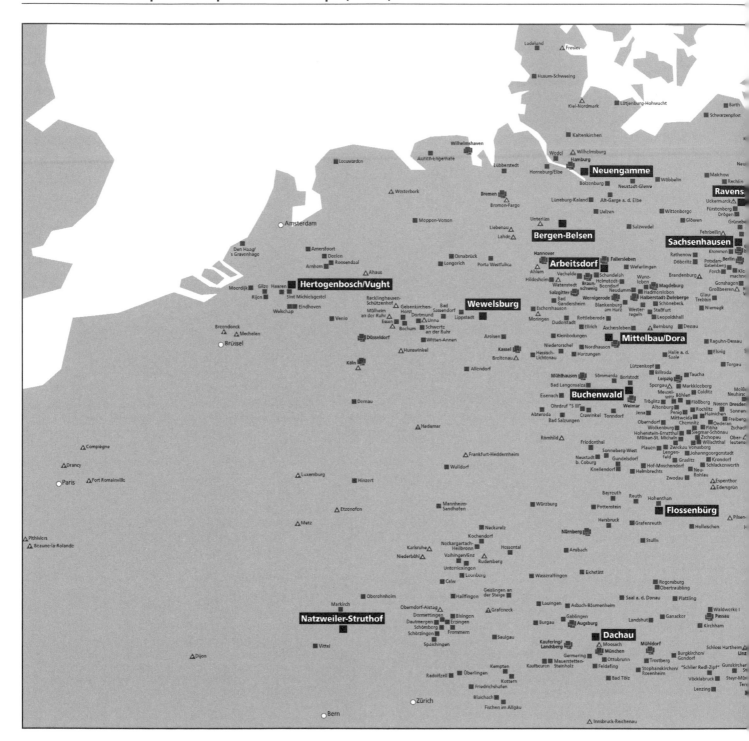

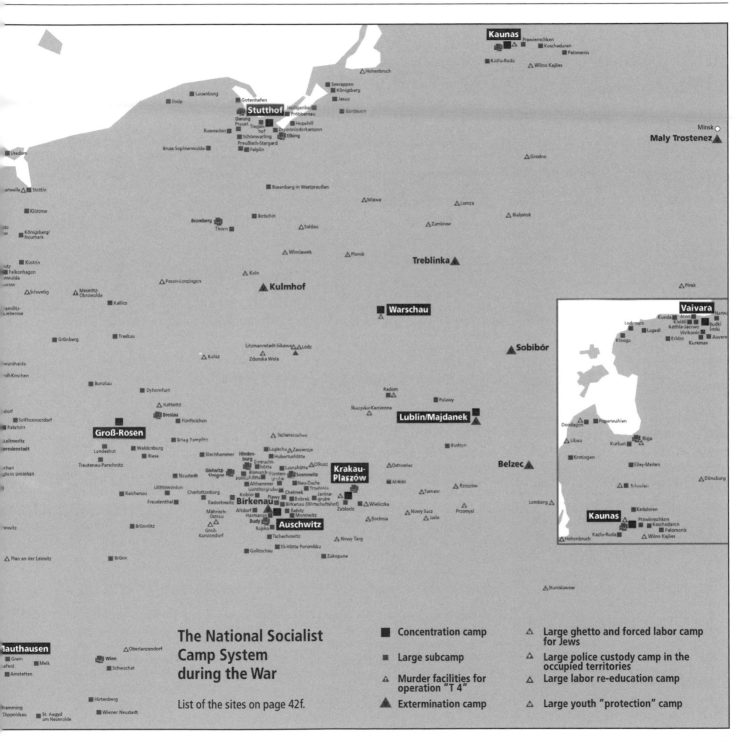

The National Socialist Camp System during the War

List of the sites on page 42f.

Symbol	Legend
■	Concentration camp
▪	Large subcamp
△	Murder facilities for operation "T 4"
▲	Extermination camp
△	Large ghetto and forced labor camp for Jews
△	Large police custody camp in the occupied territories
△	Large labor re-education camp
△	Large youth "protection" camp

Map labels include: Kaunas, Prawienschken, Koschedaren, Palomenis, Kazlu-Ruda, Wilno Kajlies, Hohenbruch, Seerappen, Königsberg, Jasau, Gerdauen, Minsk, Maly Trostenez, Lauenburg, Stolp, Gotenhafen, Heiligenbeil, Pröbbernau, Stutthof, Danzig, Praust, Tiegenhof, Zeyersniederkampen, Hopehill, Russoschin, Schönwarling, Elbing, Preußisch-Stargard, Bruss-Sophienwalde, Pelplin, Usedom, Grodno, Rosenberg in Westpreußen, erwelle, Stettin, Mlawa, Lomza, Bialystok, Klützow, Botschin, Königsberg/Neumark, Bromberg, Thorn, Soldau, Zambrow, Küstrin, Falkenhagen, Schwetig, Meseritz-Obrawalde, Kallies, Wloclawek, Plonsk, Kolo, Pinsk, Treblinka, Posen-Lenzingen, Kulmhof, Grünberg, Treskau, Warschau, Sobibór, Litzmannstadt-Sikawa, Lodz, Kalisz, Zdunska Wola, Bunzlau, Radom, Pulawy, Dyhernfurt, Rattwitz, Skazysko-Kamienna, Lublin/Majdanek, Breslau, Fünfteichen, Groß-Rosen, Briag, Rudzyn, Belzec, Landeshut, Waldenburg, Riese, Blechhammer, Lagischa, Zawierzie, Hubertushütte, Trautenau-Parschnitz, Hindenburg, Eintracht-hütte, Laurahütte, Ofkusz, Ostrowiec, Gleiwitz, Bismarck-Fürsten-grube, Sosnowitz, Neustadt, Althammer, Neu-Dachs, Reichenau, Lichtewerden, Günthergrube, Chelmek, Trzebinia, Tarnow, Rzeszów, Charlottenburg, Kobior, Bobrek, Janina-grube, Freudenthal, Radostowitz, Birkenau, Altdorf, Babitz, Wieliczka, Mährisch-Ostrau, Harmanze, Monowitz, Zablocie, Nowy Sacz, Przemysl, Brünnlitz, Budy, Bochnia, Jaslo, Groß-Kunzendorf, Rajsko, Auschwitz, Tschechowitz, Nowy Targ, Golleschau, SS-Hütte Porombka, Zakopane, Stanislawow, Plan an der Leinsitz, Brünn, Krakau-Plaszów, Mauthausen, Oberlanzendorf, Grein, Melk, Wien, Schwechat, Amstetten, Hirtenberg, Dippoldsau, St. Aegyd am Neuwalde, Wiener Neustadt

Inset map labels include: Vaivara, Narwa, Kunda, Jewe, Kiwiõli, Lodensee, Kothla-Jacrwc, Budki, Lagedi, Vivikonic, Soski, Klooga, Erides, Auvere, Kuremaa, Dondagen, Poperwahlen, Libau, Riga, Kurban, Krotingen, Elley-Meiten, Dünaburg, Schaulen, Lemberg, Kedahnen, Kaunas, Prawienschken, Koschedaren, Palomenis, Kazlu-Ruda, Wilno Kajlies, Hohenbruch

The National Socialist Camp System

List of camps marked on the map.

Concentration camp with large subcamps

Arbeitsdorf

Auschwitz
Altdorf
Althammer
Babitz
Birkenau (Wirtschaftshof)
Bismarckhütte
Blechhammer
Bobrek
Brünn
Budy
Charlottengrube
Chełmek
Eintrachthütte
Freudenthal
Fürstengrube
Gleiwitz-Steigern
Golleschau
Günthergrube
Harmenze
Hindenburg
Hubertushütte
Janinagrube
Kobiór
Lagischa
Laurahütte
Lichtewerden
Monowitz
Neu-Dachs
Neustadt
Pławy
Radostowitz
Rajsko
Sośnica
Sosnowitz
SS works Porombka
Trzebinia
Tschechowitz

Buchenwald
Abteroda
Allendorf
Altenburg
Arolsen
Aschersleben
Bad Gandersheim

Bad Langensalza
Bad Salzungen
Berlstedt
Billroda
Blankenburg am Harz
Bochum
Böhlen
Braunschweig
Colditz
Crawinkel
Dernau
Dessau
Dortmund
Duderstadt
Düsseldorf
Eisenach
Elsnig
Eschershausen
Essen
Flößberg
Gelsenkirchen-Horst
Hadmersleben
Halberstadt-Zwieberge
Halle an der Saale
Hessisch-Lichtenau
Hinzert
Jena
Kassel
Kleinbodungen
Cologne
Leipzig
Leopoldshall
Lippstadt
Lützkendorf
Magdeburg
Meuselwitz
Mühlhausen
Neustadt b. Coburg
Niederorschel
Oberndorf
Ohrdruf "S III"
Penig
Raguhn-Dessau
Schlieben
Schönebeck
Schwerte an der Ruhr
Sömmerda
Sonneberg-West
Staßfurt
Taucha
Tonndorf

Torgau
Tröglitz
Wansleben
Weferlingen
Weimar
Wernigerode
Westeregeln
Witten-Annen

Bergen-Belsen

Dachau
Augsburg
Bad Tölz
Blaichach
Burgau
Burgkirchen/Gendorf
Feldafing
Fischen im Allgäu
Friedrichshafen
Gablingen
Germering
Kaufbeuren
Kaufering/Landsberg
Kempten
Kottern
Landshut
Lauingen
Mauerstetten-Steinholz
Mühldorf
Munich
Nuremberg
Ottobrunn
Passau
Radolfzell
Saulgau
Stephanskirchen/Rosen-heim
Trostberg
Überlingen
Uttendorf/Weißsee

Flossenbürg
Bayreuth
Brüx
Chemnitz
Dresden
Eichstätt
Flöha
Freiberg
Ganacker

Grafenreuth
Graslitz
Gröditz
Gundelsdorf
Helmbrechts
Hersbruck
Hertine
Hohenstein-Ernstthal
Hohenthan
Holleischen
Hradischko
Janowitz
Johanngeorgenstadt
Jungfern-Breschan
Knellendorf
Königstein
Kirchham
Krondorf
Leitmeritz
Lengenfeld
Meißen
Mittweida
Mülsen-St. Micheln
Neu-Rohlau
Nossen
Nuremberg
Obertraubling
Oederan
Plattling
Plauen
Porschdorf
Pottenstein
Rabstein
Regensburg
Reuth
Rochlitz
Saal a.d. Donau
Schlackenwerth
Seifhennersdorf
Siegmar-Schönau
Stulln
Venusberg
Wilischthal
Wolkenburg
Würzburg
Zschachwitz
Zschopau
Zwickau

Groß-Rosen
Breslau
Brieg-Pamplitz
Brünnlitz
Bunzlau
Dyhernfurt
Fünfteichen
Groß-Koschen
Grünberg
Landeshut
Reichenau
Riese
Trautenau-Parschnitz
Treskau
Waldenburg

Hertogenbosch/Vught
Amersfoort
Arnhem
Deelen
Den Haag/'s Gravenhage
Eindhoven
Gilze-Rijen
Haaren
Leeuwarden
Moerdijk
Roosendaal
Sint Michielsgestel
Venlo
Welschap

Kaunas
Kaunas
Kazlu-Ruda
Kedahnen
Koschedaren
Palemonas
Prawienischken
Schaulen

Krakow-Plaszów
Krakow-Plaszów
Mielec
Wieliczka
Zabłocie
Zakopane

Lublin-Majdanek
Budzyń
Puławy
Radom

Mauthausen
Amstetten
Dippoldsau
Ebensee
Eisenerz
Enns
Graz
Grein
Großraming
Gunskirchen
Gusen
Hirtenberg
Klagenfurt
Lenzing
Linz
Loibl-Pass
Melk
Passau
Peggau
Schiff (Donauhafen)
"Schlier-Redl-Zipf"
Schwechat
St. Aegyd am Neuwalde
St. Lambrecht
St. Valentin
Steyr-Münichholz
Ternberg
Vöcklabruck
Waldwerke I
Wiener Neustadt

Mittelbau/Dora
Blankenburg am Harz
Ellrich
Harzungen
Kleinbodungen
Nordhausen
Rottleberode

Natzweiler-Struthof
Asbach-Bäumenheim
Bisingen
Calw
Dautmergen
Dormettingen
Erzingen
Frommern
Geislingen an der Steige
Hailfingen
Hessental
Kochendorf

Leonberg
Mannheim-Sandhofen
Markirch
Neckarelz
Neckargartach-Heilbronn
Oberehnheim
Schömberg
Schörzingen
Spaichingen
Unterriexingen
Vaihingen/Enz
Vittel
Walldorf
Wasseralfingen

Neuengamme
Ahlen
Alt-Garge a.d. Elbe
Aurich-Engerhafe
Bad Sassendorf
Boizenburg
Braunschweig
Bremen
Fallersleben
Hamburg
Hanover
Helmstedt-Beendorf
Horneburg/Elbe
Husum-Schwesing
Kaltenkirchen
Ladelund
Lengerich
Lübberstedt
Lüneburg-Kaland
Lütjenburg-Hohwacht
Meppen-Versen
Osnabrück
Porta Westfalica
Salzgitter
Salzwedel
Schandelah
Uelzen
Vechelde
Wilhemshaven
Wöbbelin

Ravensbrück
Ansbach
Barth
Drögen
Eberswalde

Finow
Fürstenberg
Grüneberg
Kallies
Karlshagen
Klützow
Königsberg/Neumark
Leipzig
Malchow
Neubrandenburg
Neustadt-Glewe
Rechlin (Retzow)
Schlieben
Schwarzenforst
St. Lambrecht

Riga-Kaiserwald
Dondangen
Elley-Meiten
Krotingen
Kurben
Poperwahlen
Riga

Sachsenhausen
Bad Saarow
Berlin
Bernau
Biesenthal
Döberitz
Falkenhagen
Ferch
Fichtengrund
Friedenthal
Fürstenwalde
Genshagen
Glau-Trebbin
Glöwen
Jamlitz-Lieberose
Kleinmachnow
Königs Wusterhausen
Kremmen
Küstrin
Neudamm
Niemegk
Oranienburg
Potsdam-Babelsberg
Rathenow
Schwarzheide
Spreehagen
Storkow

Strausberg
Trebnitz
Wittenberg

Stutthof
Botschin
Bromberg
Bruss-Sophienwalde
Danzig
Elbing
Gerdauen
Gotenhafen
Heiligenbeil
Hopehill
Jesau
Königsberg
Lauenburg
Pelplin
Praust
Preußisch-Stargard
Pröbbernau
Rosenberg in West-
preußen
Russoschin
Schönwarling
Seerappen
Stolp
Thorn
Tiegenhof
Zeyersniederkampen

Warsaw

Wewelsburg

Vaivara
Auvere
Budki
Erides
Jewe
Kiviöli
Klooga
Kothla-Jaerwe
Kunda
Kuremaa
Lagedi
Lodensee
Narwa
Soski
Vivikonie

Murder facilities
for "T 4"
Bernburg
Brandenburg
Grafeneck
Hadamar
Meseritz-Obrawalde
Schloss Hartheim
Sonnenstein

Extermination camps
Auschwitz-Birkenau
Belżec
Kulmhof
Lublin-Majdanek
Maly Trostenez
Sobibór
Treblinka

Large ghettos and
forced labor camps
for Jews
Dondangen
Dünaburg
Libau
Riga
Kaunas
Schaulen
Wilno Kajlies
Białystok
Bochnia
Grodno
Jasło
Kalisz
Koło
Krakow
Lemberg
Łódź
Łomża
Mława
Nowy Sacz
Nowy Targ
Olkusz
Ostrowiec
Pińsk
Płońsk
Przemyśl
Radom
Rzeszów
Skarżysko-Kamienna
Stanisławów

Tarnów
Tschenstochau
Warsaw
Wieliczka
Włocławek
Zambrów
Zawiercie
Zduńska Wola
Theresienstadt

Large police camps
in the occupied
territories
Barcs
Breendonck
Mechelen
Frøslev
Beaune-la-Rolande
Compiègne
Dijon
Drancy
Fort Romainville
Metz
Pithiviers
Bolzano
Fossoli
Trieste-San Sabba
Bačka Topola
Belgrade
Čoka
Pančevo
Sabac
Subotica
Zemun
Lobor
Luxemburg
Westerbork
Edersgrün
Espenthor
Theresienstadt

Large "labor
re-education camps"
Ahaus
Breitenau
Bremen-Farge
Breschan
Essen
Etzenhofen
Fehrbellin
Frankfurt-Heddernheim

Großbeeren
Groß-Kunzendorf
Hägerwelle
Hohenbruch
Hunswinkel
Innsbruck-Reichenau
Karlsruhe
Kiel-Nordmark
Cologne
Lahde
Libenau
Litzmannstadt-Sikawa
Mährisch-Ostrau
Moosach
Mühlheim an der Ruhr
Niederbühl
Oberlanzendorf
Oberleutensdorf
Oberndorf-Aistag
Pilsen-Karlow
Plan an der Leinsitz
Posen-Lenzingen
Radeberg
Rattwitz
Recklinghausen-Schüt-
zenhof
Römhild
Rudersberg
Schwetig
Soldau
Spergau
Unna
Unterlüss
Watenstedt
Wilhelmsburg
Wuhlheide

Large "youth
protection" camps
Łódź
Moringen
Uckermarck

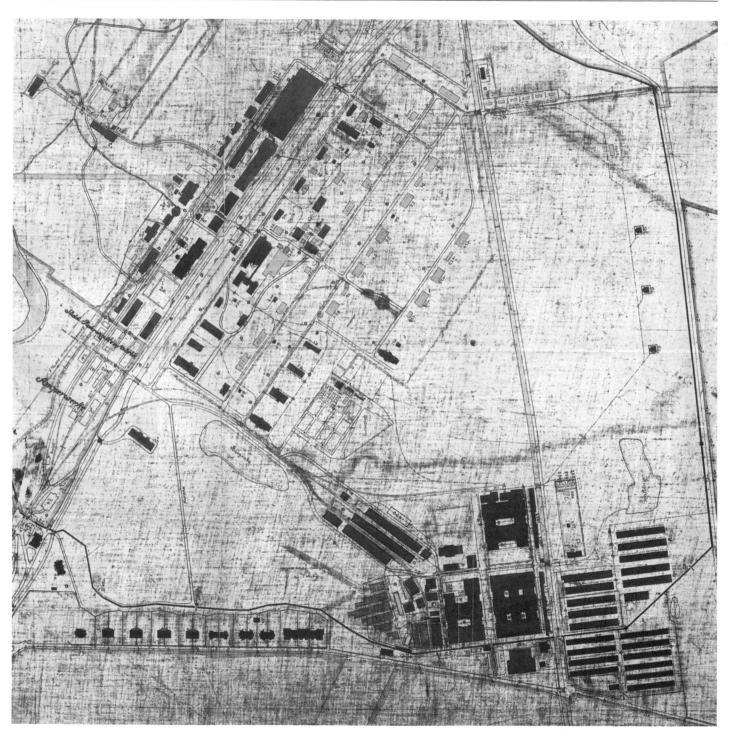

Ground plan of the Dachau concentration camp, 1933
BA Berlin

How could the National Socialist Dictatorship happen?

"Background history does not necessarily mean that everything that followed had to happen the way it did, or that it could not have turned out differently. But the seeds of anti-Semitism, racism and disregard for human dignity and democracy were sown in the period preceding the Third Reich and sprouted in a frightening way after 1933. Each of us today is shaping the prehistory of tomorrow." Chaim Schatzker

Enthusiasm and nationalism marked the beginning of World War I

In the face of mass death at the front and the want suffered at home, sectors of the German population soon became disillusioned. After four years of propagating an unstinting belief in victory and the desire to conquer, the military leadership gave up the war as lost in late summer 1918. At the same time, it attempted to shift responsibility onto those political representatives who were in favor of a negotiated peace and democratic reforms. A sailors' revolt in Kiel against a suicidal military order for the fleet to sail escalated into a revolution in November 1918 that brought about the end of Imperial Germany.

Contradictory interpretations of the causes of war, the defeat and the revolution aggravated conflicts in German society.

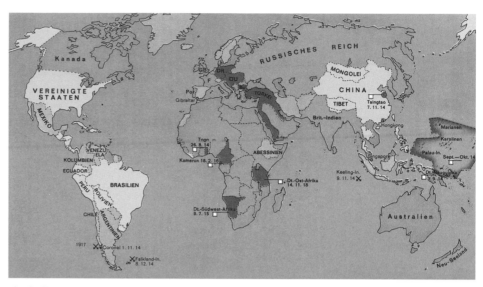

The belligerent powers in World War I World War I cost about 10 million lives. Millions of people were wounded, maimed and traumatized. dtv-Atlas

Propaganda postcard, 1915 Nationalist arrogance and imperialist goals are expressed here satirically. The star on the school desk is not an anti-Semitic allusion but a company logo.
Sammlung Karl Stehle, Munich

Paul von Hindenburg, General Chief of Staff of the Army (left), Kaiser Wilhelm II and Erich Ludendorff, First General Quartermaster of the Army Senior Command, 1917 BaPK

A scene from a World War I battlefield IWM

Revolutionaries in front of the Brandenburg Gate in Berlin, November 1918
Under the pressure of defeat in the war and the first revolutionary uprisings, Kaiser Wilhelm II abdicated. Germany became a republic. LA Berlin

Basic rights anchored in the Weimar Constitution

The constitution of the new state was adopted in the city of Weimar because Berlin appeared too insecure due to revolutionary disturbances. At elections for the National Assembly, the Social Democratic Party (SPD), the Catholic Center Party (Zentrum), and the left-liberal German Democratic Party (DDP) had gained the majority of votes and formed a coalition that supported a parliamentary republic. Adopted on August 19, 1919, the constitution guaranteed basic personal, civic and social rights.

The basic rights anchored in the Weimar Constitution
"**Article 109, paragraphs 1 and 2** All Germans are equal before the law. Men and women have the same fundamental civil rights and duties.
Article 114 Personal liberty is inviolable. Curtailment or deprivation of personal liberty by a public authority is permissible only by authority of law. Persons who have been deprived of their liberty must be informed at the latest on the following day by whose authority and for what reasons they have been held. They shall receive the opportunity without delay to submit objections to their deprivation of liberty.
Article 115 The house of every German is his sanctuary and is inviolable. Exceptions are permitted only by authority of law.
Article 117 The secrecy of letters and all postal, telegraph and telephone communication is inviolable. Exceptions are inadmissible except by national law.
Article 118, clause 1 Every German has the right, within the limits of general law, to express his opinion freely by word, in writing, in print, in picture and in any other way.
Article 123 All Germans have the right to assemble peacefully and unarmed without giving notice and without special permission.
Article 124, paragraph 1 All Germans have the right to form associations and societies for purposes not contrary to criminal law. This right cannot be limited through preventative regulations. The same applies to religious associations and societies.
Article 135, paragraph 1, clause 1 All inhabitants of the Reich enjoy full religious freedom and freedom of conscience.
Article 142, paragraph 1, clause 1 Art, science and the teaching thereof are free.
Article 151, paragraph 1, clause 1 The regulation of economic life must be compatible with the principles of justice, with the aim of attaining humane conditions of existence for all.
Article 153, paragraph 1, paragraph 2, clauses 1 and 2, paragraph 3 The right of private property is guaranteed by the Constitution. Its content and limitations are derived from the law. Expropriation of property may take place only for the benefit of society as a whole and by due process of law. It transpires with appropriate compensation, inasmuch as a Reich law does not otherwise legislate. Property obligates. It should also be of service to the common good."

The Constitution of the German Reich, August 11, 1919 (excerpt)

Poster for the National Assembly elections on January 19, 1919
The elections for the National Assembly were the first time that women were able to vote in Germany. The hope of unifying the country on the basis of a parliamentary democracy was not fulfilled however. The conflicts between the opposing political camps ran too deep.
BA Koblenz

Election poster of the German Nationalist People's Party (1924)
In 1919, former Field-Marshal Paul von Hindenburg accused the workers' movement of having denied the German military victory through their strikes and protests. The "stab-in-the-back" legend, used by the political right wing to deflect responsibility away from the monarchy for the war, defeat and the severe legacy they left behind, poisoned the political atmosphere of the Weimar Republic.
BA Berlin

Although severely shaken by political unrest and plagued by economic problems like the hyperinflation of 1923, the Weimar Republic also witnessed important modernizing impulses in all cultural areas. Sectors of the population reacted with uncertainty to such trends.

Gentry house, designed by Walter Gropius for the Bauhaus in Dessau, from the 1920s
Photo: Lucia Moholy, BHA

NSDAP flyer for the district council election in Dessau 1931, stirring up agitation against the Bauhaus school
Right wing extremists stirred resentment with vilifying slogans such as "cultural Bolshevism", "degenerate art", and "gutter literature".
After protests by conservatives had forced the Bauhaus school to leave Weimar for Dessau in 1925, it was once again forced to move following political pressure by the Nazis in 1932, this time to Berlin. Following a police raid in April 1933, it ceased working in Germany completely. BHA

Wähler und Wählerinnen Dessaus!

Der 25. Oktober gibt in Anhalt dem schaffenden Volke die Möglichkeit, den Grundstein zur Neugestaltung der politischen und wirtschaftlichen Verhältnisse zu legen. Die Not der Gemeinden ist eine Not des Volkes, entstanden aus den ungeheuren Fehlschlägen einer marxistisch-demokratisch-pazifistischen Außen- und Innenpolitik. Dem Elend und der Not durch eigene Kraft restlos zu steuern, wird den Gemeinden so lange eine Unmöglichkeit sein, so lange in Reich und Ländern nicht die letzten Vertreter der sterbenden Welt der Demokratie aus ihren Machtpositionen verschwunden und an ihre Stellen Vertreter des Volkes berufen sind, die es als ihre heilige und ernste Aufgabe ansehen, die nationalen und sozialen Belange des schaffenden Volkes zu vertreten und durchzusetzen.

Am 25. Oktober treten auch in Dessau zur Gemeindewahl erstmalig nationalsozialistische Kämpfer vor das schaffende Volk Dessaus und rufen ihm zu:

Wählt Nationalsozialisten!

Arbeit und Brot

Was wir Nationalsozialisten in der Gemeindevertretung wollen, ist

für unsere Mitbürger zu schaffen. Wir stehen grundsätzlich auf dem Standpunkte, daß diese Aufgabe nur durch eigene Kraft gelöst werden muß und nicht durch Aufnahme von Krediten, die das Gemeindevermögen aufzehren und durch eine drückende Zinslast die weitere Aufbauarbeit unmöglich machen.

Wir fordern deshalb größte Sparsamkeit im Gemeindehaushalt und sofortige Streichung sämtlicher Ausgaben, die nicht lebensnotwendig für unsere Mitbürger sind.

Wir fordern:
Sofortige Streichung sämtlicher Ausgaben für das Bauhaus.
Ausländische Lehrkräfte sind fristlos zu kündigen, da es unvereinbar ist mit der Verantwortung, die eine gute Gemeindeführung gegenüber ihren Bürgern zu tragen hat, daß deutsche Volksgenossen hungern, während Ausländer in überreichlichem Maße aus den Steuergroschen des darbenden Volkes besoldet werden. Deutsche Lehrkräfte sind durch Vermittlung der Gemeinde in Dessau oder anderwärts unterzubringen.
Für die im Bauhaus befindlichen Handwerkerschulen ist Unterkunft anderorts zu schaffen.
Der Abbruch des Bauhauses ist sofort in die Wege zu leiten.

Wir fordern:
Abbau der Stadtratsstelle Sinsel.
Die dieser Stadtratsstelle bisher obliegenden Aufgaben sind den einzelnen Ressorts zuzuteilen.

Wir fordern:
Streichung sämtlicher Aufwandsentschädigungen für städtische Beamte und Bedienstete.
Festsetzung des Oberbürgermeistergehaltes auf höchstens 9000.— RM jährlich.
Kürzung sämtlicher städtischer Gehälter über 6000.— RM jährlich um 25—30%.

Wir fordern:
Sofortige Einführung einer Filial- und Sondersteuer für Konsumgenossenschaften, Warenhäuser und Einheitspreisgeschäfte.

Wir fordern:
Laufende Winterhilfe für Kleinrentner, Kriegsbeschädigte, Kriegshinterbliebene, kinderreiche Familien und Wohlfahrtsempfänger.

Wir fordern:
Errichtung guter und billigster Kleinwohnungen für Minderbemittelte, dazu Rückführung der Hauszinssteuer zu ihrem eigentlichen Zweck, auch zur Instandsetzung der vielen alten baufälligen Häuser.

Wir fordern:
Unbedingten Mieterschutz, so lange die Wohnungsnot nicht behoben und ausreichende und billige Wohnmöglichkeiten geschaffen sind.

Wir fordern:
Zurückführung der städtischen Sparkasse auf den ihr zukommenden Zweck, nämlich die Bereitstellung langfristiger Darlehen zu niedrigen Zinssätzen an Handel- und Gewerbetreibende.

Wir betrachten diese Forderungen als Mindestforderungen und erklären, daß wir bei unserer Arbeit im Stadtparlament alle weiteren Wege rücksichtslos aufzeigen und ausschöpfen werden, die geeignet sind, Arbeit und Brot zu schaffen.

Unsere Arbeit wird unter der Losung des erwachenden Deutschlands stehen:

Gemeinnutz geht vor Eigennutz!

Wer diesen Grundsatz zur Tat umgesetzt wissen will, der

Wählt Liste 5

Liste Nationalsozialisten.   N.S.D.A.P. Ortsgruppe Dessau.

Until 1923, the republic was repeatedly threatened by uprisings, attempted coups and political murders. The extreme left strove to stage a revolutionary putsch on the Soviet model. On the radical right, monarchists, right wing conservatives and völkisch nationalists joined forces to oppose the Republic. Even though they had no alternative strategy, they were against a political direction that sought to first meet the severe terms of the Versailles Peace Treaty in order to then achieve its moderation through compromise. The radical right spread the "stab-in-the-back" legend and generally held anti-Semitic leanings. While the police, the German Army and the judiciary clamped down on leftists with brutal severity, the extreme right was treated with extreme leniency.

Uprisings and attempted putsches 1919-1923

January/March 1919
Spartacus Union, which became the Communist Party, attempts to start a revolution in Berlin, quelled by the German Army and Freikorps paramilitary.

April/May 1919
Workers' Council Republic formed by anarchists and communists in Munich, suppressed by the German Army and Freikorp paramilitary.

March 13-16, 1920
"Kapp-Lüttwitz Putsch," coup d'état staged by right wing-oriented military units in Berlin and other cities; the putsch collapses due to a general strike called by the trade unions and the failure of expected support from the German Army and state agencies to materialize.

March/April 1921
"March operation" of the Communist Party: uprising staged by armed workers in the Halle-Merseburg-Leuna area and the Ruhr Valley; bloody suppression by German Army units.

October 1, 1923
Uprising by armed Communist workers in Hamburg, suppressed by the police and the German Army.

November 8-9, 1923
Putsch by illegal military units in Küstrin, fails due to a lack of German Army support.
"Hitler Putsch" staged by NSDAP supporters and other organizations opposed to the Republic in Munich, a coup d'état against the Reich government, suppressed by the Bavarian police on November 9.

The Ehrhardt navy brigade, part of the right wing insurgent front, during the Kapp-Lüttwitz Putsch in Berlin, March 1920. The insurgent soldiers carried the naval ensign of Imperial Germany. The uprising against the republic was backed by large landowners, German Army officers, and conservative civil servants. LA Berlin

The defendants in the trial against the ringleaders of the Hitler Putsch, spring 1924
After the failed putsch attempt against the Republic on November 9, 1923, those responsible were brought to trial before a Bavarian court, where they received extremely lenient sentences. Hitler was allowed to exploit the proceedings and turn the courtroom into a political platform. He then served less than eight months of the five-year prison sentence he received. During his stay in prison Hitler wrote "Mein Kampf". Third from left: Wilhelm Frick; fifth from left: Erich Ludendorff; sixth from left: Adolf Hitler; eighth from left: Ernst Röhm. Sammlung Rudolf Herz, Munich, BayHStA

Political murders committed by right wing extremists, 1919-1922 (selected examples)

January 15, 1919

Rosa Luxemburg and Karl Liebknecht

The leaders of the radical left were murdered by right wing Freikorps paramilitary units. SAPMO

February 21, 1919

Kurt Eisner

The Bavarian Prime Minister and USPD (Independent Socialist) politician was shot by Anton Graf Arco-Valley, a Bavarian Army lieutenant with right wing leanings. Photo: Germaine Krull, Sammlung Rudolf Herz, Munich

August 26, 1921

Matthias Erzberger

The Center Party politician was murdered by members of the right wing extremist Organization Consul (O.C.). Erzberger had signed the cease fire with the victorious powers on November 11, 1918. BA Berlin

24. Juni 1922

Walther Rathenau

In his office as Secretary of State, the industrialist, politician and philosopher was one of the outstanding representatives of the Republic. Assassins from the Organization Consul (O.C.) shot him as symbolic figure for the republic and because he was a Jew. BaPK

National Socialism merged and radicalized a number of different political positions that were widespread in German society, in particular, nationalism, imperialism and Social Darwinism, as well as resentments against liberalism, democracy, and the socialist workers' movement.

The ideas of the Nazi movement strove towards realizing a "racially pure national body". All elements that "weakened" or did not fit into this body were to be removed. Such notions gave expression to a racism that classified and treated people as superior or inferior according to biological characteristics. Anti-Semitic images and notions that portrayed Jews as the enemy formed the crux of National Socialist ideology.

Hatred of Jews was a centuries-old tradition in Germany. At first, discrimination against Jews was religiously and socially motivated. Beginning in the 19th century, more and more racially based "arguments" were put forward. National Socialism propagated a radical biological anti-Semitism.

"The Jewish Paradise"
Caricature in the "Deutsche Witzblatt", 1922
This hateful illustration combines the anti-Semitic stereotype of "Jewish Bolshevism" with that of the "Jewish violation of young German womanhood". BaPK

"Marxism is the guardian angel of capitalism", NSDAP poster for the Reichstag elections of November 1932

This anti-Semitic depiction illustrates the double image of the Jews as enemies, combining Jewish capitalists with the socialist workers' movement "steered by Jews". BA Koblenz

---

3. We demand land and territory (colonies) to feed our people and settle our surplus population.

4. Only members of the nation may be citizens of the State. Only those of German blood, whatever their creed, may be members of the nation. Accordingly, no Jew can be a member of the nation…

8. All further non-German immigration must be prevented. We demand that all non-Germans who have entered Germany after August 2, 1914, shall be required to leave the Reich forthwith.

NSDAP party program of February 24, 1920 (excerpt)

Jews and members of other nations and races who stand in opposition to Germandom may not acquire any membership rights.

Statute of the German National Retail Clerks Association (DHV), June 9, 1928 (excerpt)

The German National Retail Clerks Association was the largest white-collar organization in the Weimar Republic. Since the Imperial era, many bourgeois clubs and associations had denied membership to Jews.

The phase of economic stabilization in Germany that had begun in 1924 came to an abrupt end in the fall of 1929 when the worldwide economic crisis set in. The number of unemployed rose rapidly. Millions of people were without work and received hardly any financial support. Many starved. The economic catastrophe worked in favor of anti-democratic forces. Particularly the National Socialists, but also the Communists, were able to mobilize an increasing number of followers and voters by presenting themselves as "rescuers in times of need".

Unemployed standing in line in front of the employment office in Hanover, around 1931
Photo: Walter Ballhause, DHM

"Our last hope: Hitler", NSDAP election poster, April 1932
The often despairing unemployed were the preferred target of National Socialist propaganda.
BayHStA

The development of unemployment in the German Reich, 1921-1933
Möller, Weimar

■ Number out of work

■ In percentage of wage earners

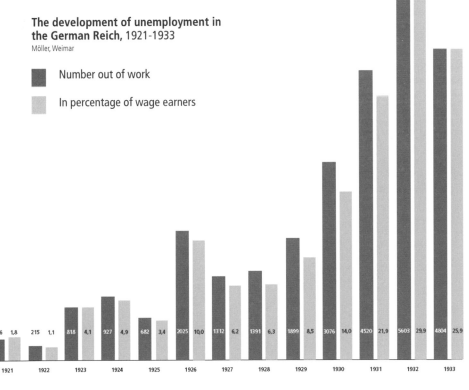

Year	Number out of work	In percentage of wage earners
1921	346	1,8
1922	215	1,1
1923	818	4,1
1924	927	4,9
1925	682	3,4
1926	2025	10,0
1927	1312	6,2
1928	1391	6,3
1929	1899	8,5
1930	3076	14,0
1931	4520	21,9
1932	5603	29,9
1933	4804	25,9

In 1920, the German Workers' Party (DAP), founded in Munich in 1919, was renamed the National Socialist German Workers' Party (NSDAP). Adolf Hitler became party leader with dictatorial powers.

Temporarily banned after Hitler's failed coup d'état in 1923, the NSDAP remained a peripheral political force during the stable years of the Weimar Republic. This changed dramatically with the onset of the world economic crisis. In the Reichstag elections of September 1930, the NSDAP succeeded in increasing its share of the vote from 2.6 per cent to 18.3 per cent; in the Reichstag elections of July 1932, the NSDAP emerged as the strongest party with 37.3 per cent of the vote. The party made use of both brutal violence against its opponents as well as modern propaganda methods and tactics. The party succeeded in evoking the impression that it alone was capable of meeting the divergent interests of a number of social groups. By mobilizing resentment and exploiting images of threatening enemies, the National Socialists were able to conceal the internal contradictions riddling their political demands. Conservative power elites in the state apparatus, especially large landowners and industrialists, regarded the NSDAP as a partner in the struggle against the despised republic.

Parade by the SA past Adolf Hitler at the second NSDAP party congress in Weimar on July 4, 1926 Photo: Heinrich Hoffmann, Slg. Rudolf Herz, München

NSDAP poster for the Reichstag elections of November 1932 BayHStA

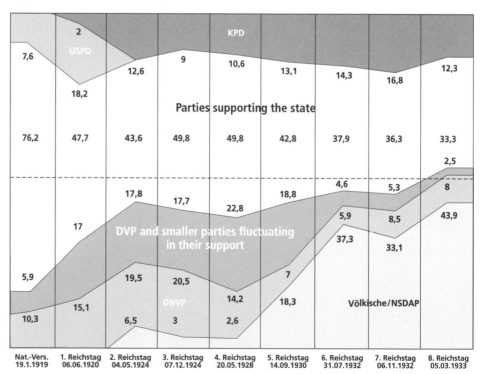

Election results for the National Assembly and the Reichstag, 1919-1933 Schulze, Weimar

54

The SPD and the Center Party sought to protect the constitution in the final crisis period of the Weimar Republic, although for a time the Center also succumbed to the illusion that this could succeed by integrating the NSDAP into a governing coalition. The left-liberal German Democratic Party (DDP) had become an insignificant political factor. The Communists (KPD) fought not only the National Socialists but also the Weimar Republic. As a result, the workers' movement remained split in its resistance against Hitler's party.

Center Party poster for the Reichstag elections of 1932

The tower, the Center's political symbol, is depicted as a refuge from the opponents of freedom and order. However, both the NSDAP and the KPD had already outstripped the Center in the Reichstag elections of 1930. Reich Chancellor Brüning had governed without a parliamentary majority, supported by emergency decrees issued by President Hindenburg, who however, then dropped him shortly before the first Reichstag elections held in 1932. BA Koblenz

SPD poster for the Reichstag elections of September 1930

Here the KPD, the NSDAP and the Stahlhelm are depicted as enemies of democracy. AdsD, Seliger-Archiv

KPD poster for the Reichstag elections of July 1932

The anti-fascist rhetoric employed by the KPD resonated with sectors of the young working-class. Nonetheless, the party lacked clear (democratic) prospects capable of winning a majority. DHM

The severe economic crisis exacerbated social tensions. Conservative-authoritarian political forces used this to undermine the parliamentary system. A lack of democratic consciousness and the inability to form a majority in the Reichstag meant that, from 1930, the Reich Chancellor governed on the basis of emergency decrees issued by the Reich President. In this way, parliament was largely excluded from the legislative process and the changing of governments. A state of emergency became the rule. In both of the two Reichstag elections held in 1932, the NSDAP emerged as the strongest party. A circle of army generals, heavy industrialists and large landowners pressured Reich President Paul von Hindenburg into appointing Adolf Hitler Reich Chancellor.

When this finally happened on January 30, 1933, the National Socialists began establishing their dictatorship.

Adolf Hitler in talks with representatives of heavy industry, 1932   Bay SB

Decree issued by the Reich President for the Protection of People and State (Reichstag Fire Decree), February 28, 1933 (excerpt)
The decree issued immediately after the Reichstag fire rescinded the civil rights anchored in the Weimar constitution, including those concerning individual liberty. This enabled the practically unrestricted imposition of police protective custody. The "Reichstag Fire Decree" was thus the "judicial basis" for the concentration camp system. Jurist Ernst Fraenkel called this decree the "constitutional charter" of the National Socialist state.
RGBl. I, 1933

-4.3.1933

83

Reichsgesetzblatt

Teil I

| 1933 | Ausgegeben zu Berlin, den 28. Februar 1933 | Nr. 17 |

Inhalt: Verordnung des Reichspräsidenten zum Schutz von Volk und Staat. Vom 28. Februar 1933 ...... S. 83

Verordnung des Reichspräsidenten zum Schutz von Volk und Staat. Vom 28. Februar 1933.

Auf Grund des Artikels 48 Abs. 2 der Reichsverfassung wird zur Abwehr kommunistischer staatsgefährdender Gewaltakte folgendes verordnet:

§ 1

Die Artikel 114, 115, 117, 118, 123, 124 und 153 der Verfassung des Deutschen Reichs werden bis auf weiteres außer Kraft gesetzt. Es sind daher Beschränkungen der persönlichen Freiheit, des Rechts der freien Meinungsäußerung, einschließlich der Pressefreiheit, des Vereins- und Versammlungsrechts, Eingriffe in das Brief-, Post-, Telegraphen- und Fernsprechgeheimnis, Anordnungen von Haussuchungen und von Beschlagnahmen sowie Beschränkungen des Eigentums auch außerhalb der sonst hierfür bestimmten gesetzlichen Grenzen zulässig.

§ 2

Werden in einem Lande die zur Wiederherstellung der öffentlichen Sicherheit und Ordnung nötigen Maßnahmen nicht getroffen, so kann die Reichsregierung insoweit die Befugnisse der obersten Landesbehörde vorübergehend wahrnehmen.

§ 3

Die Behörden der Länder und Gemeinden (Gemeindeverbände) haben den auf Grund des § 2 erlassenen Anordnungen der Reichsregierung im Rahmen ihrer Zuständigkeit Folge zu leisten.

§ 4

Wer den von den obersten Landesbehörden oder den ihnen nachgeordneten Behörden zur Durchführung dieser Verordnung erlassenen Anordnungen oder den von der Reichsregierung gemäß § 2 erlassenen Anordnungen zuwiderhandelt oder wer zu solcher Zuwiderhandlung auffordert oder anreizt, wird, soweit nicht die Tat nach anderen Vorschriften mit einer schwereren Strafe bedroht ist, mit Gefängnis nicht unter einem Monat oder mit Geldstrafe von 150 bis zu 15 000 Reichsmark bestraft.

Wer durch Zuwiderhandlung nach Abs. 1 eine gemeine Gefahr für Menschenleben herbeiführt, wird mit Zuchthaus, bei mildernden Umständen mit Gefängnis nicht unter sechs Monaten und, wenn die Zuwiderhandlung den Tod eines Menschen verursacht, mit dem Tode, bei mildernden Umständen mit Zuchthaus nicht unter zwei Jahren bestraft. Daneben kann auf Vermögenseinziehung erkannt werden.

Wer zu einer gemeingefährlichen Zuwiderhandlung (Abs. 2) auffordert oder anreizt, wird mit Zuchthaus, bei mildernden Umständen mit Gefängnis nicht unter drei Monaten bestraft.

§ 5

Mit dem Tode sind die Verbrechen zu bestrafen, die das Strafgesetzbuch in den §§ 81 (Hochverrat), 229 (Giftbeibringung), 307 (Brandstiftung), 311 (Explosion), 312 (Überschwemmung), 315 Abs. 2 (Beschädigung von Eisenbahnanlagen), 324 (gemeingefährliche Vergiftung) mit lebenslangem Zuchthaus bedroht.

Mit dem Tode oder, soweit nicht bisher eine schwerere Strafe angedroht ist, mit lebenslangem Zuchthaus oder mit Zuchthaus bis zu 15 Jahren wird bestraft:

1. Wer es unternimmt, den Reichspräsidenten oder ein Mitglied oder einen Kommissar der Reichsregierung oder einer Landesregierung zu töten oder wer zu einer solchen Tötung auffordert, sich erbietet, ein solches Erbieten annimmt oder eine solche Tötung mit einem anderen verabredet;

2. wer in den Fällen des § 115 Abs. 2 des Strafgesetzbuchs (schwerer Aufruhr) oder des § 125 Abs. 2 des Strafgesetzbuchs (schwerer Landfriedensbruch) die Tat mit Waffen oder in bewußtem und gewolltem Zusammenwirken mit einem Bewaffneten begeht;

3. wer eine Freiheitsberaubung (§ 239) des Strafgesetzbuchs in der Absicht begeht, sich des der Freiheit Beraubten als Geisel im politischen Kampfe zu bedienen.

§ 6

Diese Verordnung tritt mit dem Tage der Verkündung in Kraft.

Berlin, den 28. Februar 1933.

Der Reichspräsident
von Hindenburg

Der Reichskanzler
Adolf Hitler

Der Reichsminister des Innern
Frick

Der Reichsminister der Justiz
Dr. Gürtner

Herausgegeben vom Reichsministerium des Innern. — Gedruckt in der Reichsdruckerei, Berlin.

Reichsgesetzbl. 1933 I   25

The Road to Dictatorship 1933

January 30 Hitler appointed Reich Chancellor ("seizure of power")

February 28 Basic rights are revoked ("Reichstag Fire Decree")

March 9 The state governments are forced into line ("Gleichschaltung"): Franz Ritter von Epp, "commissioned by the Reich", takes over government affairs in Bavaria

March 21 – State ceremony in the Potsdam Garrison Church to publicly demonstrate the reconciliation between the national-conservative camp and the National Socialist movement ("Day of Potsdam")

– "Special Courts" are set up for political offenses; a decree is passed against the spreading of "untrue claims" about the government ("Treachery Law")

– The first concentration camps are established

March 24 The Reichstag empowers the executive to pass laws and change the constitution without requiring parliamentary approval ("Enabling Act"); only the SPD votes against the bill; the KPD deputies are either already under arrest or have disappeared underground

April 7 Jewish and "politically unreliable" civil servants are dismissed under the "Law for the Restoration of the Professional Civil Service"

May 2 Trade union buildings are occupied and the unions crushed

May 10 Public burning of books written by leftist, democratic and Jewish authors

July 14 The NSDAP becomes the official party of the state; all other parties are banned or disband themselves

1934

January 30 The sovereignty of the Reich states is abolished

June 30 SA leaders and political rivals are murdered ("Röhm Putsch")

August 1 The offices of Reich President and Reich Chancellor are merged into one

August 2 Reich President Hindenburg dies; the army swears an oath of loyalty to Hitler, who assumes the title "Führer and Reich Chancellor"

Communists and Social Democrats taken into "protective custody" in the Friedrichstrasse SA barracks in Berlin, April 1, 1933 BaPK

"Protective Custody"

Under the legal system of the Weimar Republic, it was permitted to arrest people in order to protect the state during outbreaks of internal unrest. Their arrest was then investigated by the courts and subjected to a fixed time limit. Under the Nazi regime, imposing unlimited "protective custody" was made possible by the "Reichstag Fire Decree". This decree legitimized the arrest of political opponents of National Socialism. The political police authorities (later unified as the Gestapo) issued the protective custody warrants. There was no means of legal redress or appeal. The arrested persons were imprisoned primarily in concentration camps. Deprived of their legal rights and protections, anyone taken into "protective custody" was at the mercy of the Nazi institutions of persecution.

Report in the Augsburg "Neue Nationalzeitung" (New National News) on the establishment of the Dachau concentration camp, March 21, 1933 KZ-Gst. Dachau

Das erste Konzentrationslager bei Dachau errichtet!
Die neue Heimat für 5000 kommunistische und sozialdemokratische Volksschädlinge

München, 20. März. Polizeipräsident Himmler versicherte gegenüber der Presse am Montag, daß die Schutzhaft in den einzelnen Fällen nich länger aufrechterhalten werde, als notwendig sei. Es sei aber selbstverständlich, daß das Material, das in ungeahnter Menge beschlagnahmt wurde, zur Sichtung längere Zeit benötigt. Die Polizei werde dabei nur aufgehalten, wenn dauernd angefragt werde, wann dieser oder jener Schutzhäftling freigelassen werde. Jede Anfrage koste auf diese Weise dem Schutzhäftling praktisch einen Tag länger Haft, weil die Behörden in der Arbeit aufgehalten werden.

Wie unrichtig die vielfach verbreiteten Gerüchte über die Behandlung von Schutzhäftlingen seien, gehe daraus hervor, daß einigen Schutzhäftlingen, die es wünschen, wie z. B. Dr. Gerlich und Freih. v. Aretin, priesterlicher Zuspruch genehmigt worden sei.

Ferner teilte der Polizeipräsident mit, daß in der Nähe von Dachau am Mittwoch das erste Konzentrationslager eröffnet werde mit einem Fassungsvermögen von 5000 Menschen. Hier würden die gesamten Kommunisten, Reichsban-

ner- und sonstigen marxistischen Funktionäre zusammengezogen, da es auf die Dauer nicht möglich sei, daß man den Staatsapparat so sehr belaste. Anderseits könne man auch bei den kommunistischen Funktionären nicht an eine Freilassung denken, weil sie, wie sich in einzelnen Fällen ergeben habe, sofort wieder weiterhetzen, sobald sie in Freiheit gesetzt seien.

Scharfes Vorgehen gegen falsche Berichterstattung
Neuregelung der Vergebung der amtlichen Bekanntmachungen — Scharfes Vorgehen gegen falsche Berichterstattung durch ausländische Pressevertreter

München, 20. März. Staatssekretär Esser teilte in der Pressebesprechung am Montag mit, daß bereits am Dienstag eine Verordnung erscheinen werde, wonach die Vergebung der amtlichen Bekanntmachungen an die Tageszei-

"The first Concentration Camp near Dachau has been set up!
A new home for 5,000 Communist and Social Democratic national pests.
... Here all Communist, Reichsbanner and other marxist functionaries will be collected because it is not possible to burden the State System with them over the longer term..."

The Beginnings of the Dachau Concentration Camp, 1933

The Dachau concentration camp was the only camp to have existed throughout the entire twelve years of Nazi rule. In the early years it was the largest and best known concentration camp. The name "Dachau" soon spread fear and terror throughout Germany.

New prisoners in front of the camp headquarters, May 24, 1933
Photo: SS, BA Ludwigsburg

On March 20, 1933, Heinrich Himmler, commissary Police President in Munich, announced the establishment of a concentration camp for the arrested political opponents at a press conference.

The concentration camp was set up in the buildings of an unused gunpowder and munitions factory near Dachau. The camp was initially placed under the command of the regional Bavarian police. The first prisoner transport arrived on March 22, 1933. Photo: SS, BA Ludwigsburg

Prisoners marching to the camp kitchen, May 24, 1933 Photo: SS, BA Ludwigsburg

In order to break the personality and will of the new prisoners, they were brutally mishandled upon their arrival in the camp. Over the years, the reception procedure took on increasingly devious and brutal forms.

The Schubraum

In 1938 the admission procedure for new arrivals was transferred to the so-called Schubraum (literally "batch room," where consignments of new prisoners were administratively processed). Here they had to hand over their clothing and possessions. Naked, they were then sent to the prisoner baths.

> "You have no rights, no honor and no protection. You're a pile of shit, and will be treated as such."
>
> Part of the address usually given by protective custody camp leader Josef Jarolin to the new prisoners. Zámečník, That was Dachau.

The first prisoner transport at the entrance to the Dachau concentration camp, March 22, 1933
StadtA Munich

Albert Theis (1920) Albert Theis served in the Luxembourg "Volunteers Company", which was forcibly incorporated into the German police force in 1940. Because of their refusal to serve in partisan areas in Slovenia and to swear allegiance to Hitler, 44 Luxemburgers were arrested and deported to various concentration camps. Seventeen of them were executed in Sachsenhausen.

On March 25, 1942, Albert Theis arrived in Dachau with 16 colleagues. Every year during their imprisonment they were each ordered to swear allegiance to Hitler. They always refused the oath.
KZ-GSt. Dachau

A horde of brutal SS men jumped into the wagons and drove us out onto the platform with blows, where swarms of heavily-armed guards were milling around. Whoever did not climb quickly enough into the waiting trucks was beaten up. ... Once we had arrived in the camp, the same scene as at the station was played out all over again in front of the headquarters... Popp, Another Transport.

Arrival of the first Austrian prisoners
When we arrived in Dachau and had been dragged from the train to the camp and beaten into a corner there, a kind of public interrogation began from a horde of so-called officers ... Every nasty joke they made received applause from their SS audience, and every one of their humiliating obscenities met with raucous laughter. Kalmár, Time without Mercy.

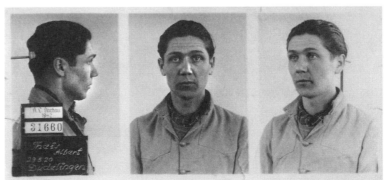

Police records photo of Albert Theis, 1942 Private ownership

German Communists and Social Democrats were the first prisoners sent to the Dachau concentration camp; later, politicians from parties of the political center and monarchists were also interned in Dachau.

Report in the "Neue Augsburger Zeitung" on a raid (on the right) against Communists in a working-class neighborhood in Augsburg, April 11, 1933.
KZ-Gst. Dachau

Im „beſetzten Gebiet"
Die Kommuniſtenrazzia links der Werlach

Originalaufnahmen der „Neuen Augsburger Zeitung"

Links oben: Polizeitrupps im abgesperrten Viertel. — Mitte: Polizeiautos vor der Peſtalozzi-Straße, von wo aus die Aktion geleitet wurde. — Links unten: Die abgesperrte Peſtalozzi-Straße. — Rechts oben: Eines der beſchmierten Häuſer. — Rechts unten: Leibesviſitation.

Social Democratic functionaries and trade unionists in the Dachau concentration camp Josef Simon, chairman of the shoemakers' union, carries the humiliating sign "I am a class-conscious S.P.D. bigwig"; after initially refusing, Simon only relented to the photograph after being threatened with physical violence. Photo: SS, July 1, 1933, KZ-Gst. Dachau

Josef Simon
(1865-1949)
Josef Simon, a Nuremberg Social Democrat, trade unionist and Reichstag deputy, was sent to the Dachau concentration camp in June 1933. Released in January 1934, he was again imprisoned in Dachau for four months in 1935.
Photo: around 1930, Archiv Walter Simon, Nuremberg

Franz Stenzer
(1900-1933)
Franz Stenzer was a member of the central committee of the KPD and a Reichstag deputy. Arrested at the end of May 1933, he was sent to the Dachau concentration camp, where he was subjected to severe mistreatment. On August 22, 1933, SS men dragged him out his detention cell and shot him "while trying to escape". Photo: 1930, KZ-Gst. Dachau

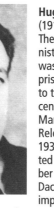

Hugo Jakusch
(1911-1991)
The young Communist Hugo Jakusch was among the first prisoners brought to the Dachau concentration camp on March 22, 1933. Released in March 1935, he was arrested again in November 1936 and sent to Dachau. He remained imprisoned in a number of concentration camps until the end of the war. He was highly respected as a Capo for his courageous defense of fellow prisoners. KZ-Gst. Dachau

On April 11, 1933, the SS took over the command of the Dachau concentration camp from the regional police. Their reign of terror over the camp began immediately.

Rudolf Benario, one of the four men shot, political economist from Nuremberg, arrived at the Dachau concentration camp on April 11, 1933; he was murdered the following day. Photo: private ownership

A beating as "welcome"
In 1933-34, newly admitted Jewish prisoners, well-known political functionaries and often indiscriminately all "new arrivals" were "welcomed" with 25 or more blows of an oxtail whip. The Jewish prisoners Wilhelm Aron and Louis Schloss, as well as the political prisoners Hugo Handschuch and Josef Amuschel, did not survive the "welcome".

Wilhelm Aron, (see photo right)
The law clerk from Bamberg was beaten so horrendously because of his Jewish ancestry upon his arrival on May 15, 1933, that he died four days later.

Flucht aus dem Konzentrationslager Dachau
Drei Kommunisten erschossen

Am Mittwoch nachmittag unternahmen, wie der Polizeibericht mitteilt, vier im Konzentrationslager Dachau untergebrachte Kommunisten einen Fluchtversuch. Da sie auf die Haltrufe der Posten nicht hörten, gaben die Posten Schüsse ab, wobei drei Kommunisten getötet und einer schwer verletzt wurde.

The shooting of four prisoners sets an example Already on the second day under the SS administration, on April 12, 1933 after evening roll call, the SS led four Jewish prisoners out of the camp, namely Dr. Rudolf Benario, Ernst Goldmann, Erwin Kahn and Arthur Kahn, and shot them "while trying to escape". Arthur Kahn was seriously wounded and died in hospital. NAZ, April 15, 1933

Group photo of the Bamberg Socialist Workers' Youth, 1931, with Wilhelm Aron in the middle (wearing a bowtie). StA Bamberg

Hugo Burkhard
The Jewish prisoner Hugo Burkhard depicts the "welcome" he received upon his arrival at the Dachau concentration camp on June 3, 1933:

Then they dragged me to a wooden trestle … strapped my hands and feet together and tore the clothes off my body; they beat me continuously with a club and the so-called ox whip (a smoked oxtail tendon); I clenched my teeth in pain, bit my tongue, but I still had the strength to bear this dreadful torture without uttering a sound … It was probably the most intense pain that a fully conscious person could bear and I'll never forget it for the rest of my life…
Burkhard, Just dance Jew.

The administrator Vogel …handed …me a two-meter long rope and – pointing to the rope – said "should you start to have any doubts, you can always use this".
In the so-called bunker (the special detention building) the prisoners were driven to suicide or murdered. Suicide was given as the cause of death. Beimler, In the Hands of Hitler's Hell-Hounds.

The camp regulations (the so-called special regulations) of May 1933 represented an attempt to turn the Dachau concentration camp into a state within a state, with its own laws and own executive and judicial authority. This failed however, due to the intervention of the Bavarian judiciary. Himmler was forced to dismiss Wäckerle as camp commandant.

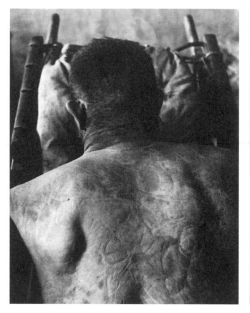
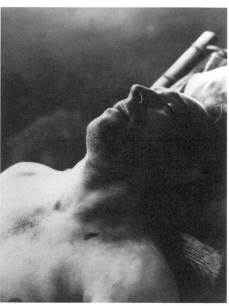

Photos of Sebastian Nefzger (1900-1933), murdered in the Dachau concentration camp, taken during the forensic postmortem examination, May 30, 1933 Photo from the investigation files, StA Munich

Hilmar Wäckerle (1899-1941), the first camp commandant at Dachau, always came to the camp with a whip in his hand and a German shepherd at his side. Photo: SS files, BA Berlin

Karl Wintersberger, head prosecuting attorney at the Munich II district court, was a conscientious and courageous civil servant. He launched investigations into the death cases occurring in the Dachau concentration camp and ordered autopsies. At the beginning of June 1933, he charged Wäckerle and a few other SS men from Dachau with murder or accessory to murder. The SS and SA leadership were able to prevent court proceedings taking place. BayStminJ

Nazi Propaganda

3.5

From the very beginning the press reported on the Dachau concentration camp. Nazi propaganda presented the camp as an institution where the prisoners, living in humane conditions, were to be re-educated, in particular through work. At the same time, the propaganda expressly sought to portray the camp prisoners as repulsive, degenerate individuals who had to be removed from German society.

Prisoners building the "swimming pool" The "swimming pool" for prisoners was in reality a dirty, stinking pond. Swimming was prohibited due to the risk of infection.
Photo: SS, "Münchner Illustrierte Presse", July 16, 1933

Prisoners on their way to work
Photo: SS, "Münchner Illustrierte Presse", July 16, 1933

Through Dachau to National Socialism
Eighty to ninety per cent of these prisoners … are bastardized, hybrid monsters with an admixture of Jewish, Negro, Mongol or – only the Devil knows – some other sort of blood. (…) They need not die, but they should die out. (…) When this diseased--because foreign--part of our German blood is finally completely exterminated and has disappeared without a trace, only then will the future of our people be secured! …All in all, today Dachau is no longer just an episode, but a program and a watchword for all those who are neither of good faith nor good will: "Through Dachau to National Socialism and the Third Reich!"
NSDAP Reichstag deputy Hans Dietrich, "Coburger Zeitung", June 28, 1933

Drei typische Vertreter des Untermenschentums im Konzentrationslager Dachau.
Kommunist   Arbeitsscheuer   Berufsverbrecher

Nazi propaganda abused regime opponents as human "bastards"
With disparaging descriptions of selected prisoners, Nazi propaganda tried to present the prisoners as "inferior". Photo: SS, "Illustrierter Beobachter", December 3, 1936. BaySB

Tours of the camp by German and foreign delegations were an important component of Nazi propaganda. The aim of the tours was twofold: first, the visitors were to be shown an orderly model camp; and second, they were to be convinced of the racial "inferiority" of the prisoners.

The cynical motto on the roof of the maintenance building
There is one path to freedom. Its milestones are obedience, honesty, cleanliness, sobriety, hard work, discipline, truthfulness and love of the fatherland. Photo: SS, 1939, KZ-Gst. Dachau

The delegations were shown: the modern kitchen, the showers for 150 persons, the first two, well-equipped infirmary barracks, the canteen, the library and an SS museum. The extreme cleanliness and order was intended to impress the visitors. NIO

In 1933 over 80 concentration camps were set up. Their function was to provide an area "outside the jurisdiction of the law" that isolated political opponents, allowing them to be neutralized and eliminated. The majority of camps were disbanded in the following months. In 1935 Hitler ordered that the camp system be retained and extended as a national political instrument of terror.

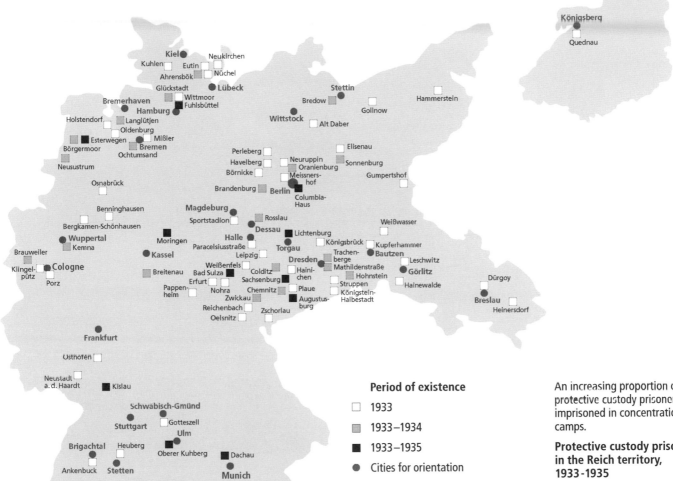

Period of existence

- ☐ 1933
- ◼ (gray) 1933–1934
- ■ 1933–1935
- ● Cities for orientation

Map of the concentration camp sites, 1933-1935 KZ-Gst. Dachau

An increasing proportion of the protective custody prisoners were imprisoned in concentration camps.

Protective custody prisoners in the Reich territory, 1933-1935

April 1933	ca.	50 000
July 1933	ca.	26 789
October 1933	ca.	22 000
April 1934	ca.	9 000
End of 1934	ca.	3 000
Mid- 1935	ca.	4 700

With the start of preparations for war the concentration camp system was extended. New, larger camps were built. The number of prisoners rose visibly. Besides political opponents, the arrests were now increasingly aimed at "social and racial-hygiene" targets. Economic aspects gained in importance: the prisoners were exploited in SS-owned workshops.

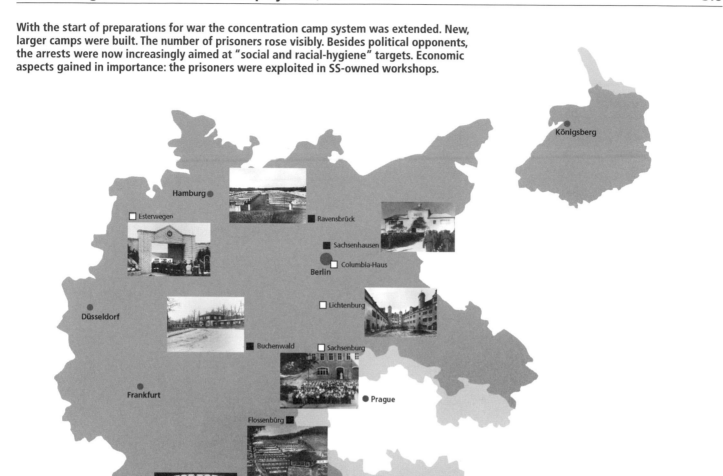

Concentration camp prisoners, 1936-1939

Fall 1936	ca.	4 800
September 1937	ca.	7 500
October 1938	ca.	24 000
November 1938	ca.	60 000
September 1939	ca.	21 400

☐ Concentration camps disbanded before the war

■ Concentration camps in existence until 1945

● Cities for orientation

Map of the concentration camps,* 1936-1939
*Under the command of the Inspectorate for Concentration Camps   KZ-Gst. Dachau

In 1937-1938 the inmates had to tear down the prisoner camp and build a considerably larger camp complex that was designed to accommodate 6,000 prisoners. The Jourhaus (entrance gate building), the service building, the detention block (bunker) and 34 barracks were among the newly constructed buildings. Located next to the prisoner camp was the SS area, which was also extended.

> The year 1937 was a horribly hard year for us Dachauers. That was when construction of the new large camp, soon notorious throughout the whole world, began. 4 o'clock wake up, 5:30 line up for roll call, 6 o'clock work began. At six in the evening work was over, and roll call followed again. The penal company had to work even longer, until dark. Work the whole day without a break, workdays, Sundays and holiday, it made no difference at all. Until May 1938 there was not a single day off, except for Christmas Day.
>
> Hübsch, Island of Military Law (Insel des Standrechts), on the period when the camp was enlarged; he was imprisoned in the Dachau concentration camp 1937-1945. FfZg

Prisoners doing construction work, July 20, 1938 Photo: SS, BA Ludwigsburg

Two Jewish prisoners doing construction work (front right: Otto Altendorf, b. 1894), July 1938 Otto Altendorf arrived in the Dachau concentration camp from Vienna on June 3, 1938. From Dachau he was sent to the Buchenwald concentration camp in September of the same year. After his release in May 1939, he succeeded in immigrating to the United States. Photo: SS, BA Ludwigsburg

The Jewish prisoner Emanuel Stambler (b. 1889) digging a ditch in July 1938. Emanuel Stambler was sent to the Dachau concentration camp in June 1938. In September of the same year he was taken to the Buchenwald concentration camp. After his release he managed to immigrate to Shanghai. Photo: SS, BA Ludwigsburg

After the munitions factory was closed down in 1919, unemployment and poverty were rife in Dachau. Quite a few residents therefore welcomed the establishment of a concentration camp close to the city, hoping that this would improve the economic situation. Until the mid-1930s there were close economic ties between the city and the camp. However the anticipated economic upturn never occurred.

Trade and development, business and industry have experienced a strong recovery due to construction work and not least due to the two SS camps (K.L.D. and II. SS Regiment "Deutschland") located in the direct vicinity of Dachau. It is thanks solely to this recovery that the past and current fiscal years have visibly improved. This improvement will, in all probability, not only continue, but even increase to some extent. The hoped-for increase in tax revenues etc. have not, however, had an effect on the city and its finances on the scale that was expected, so that in summary and in conclusion it can be stated: Dachau and its administration, as a National Socialist-run community, has faith in the future and goes to work supported and reinforced by this faith.

Memorandum from Dachau mayor Lambert Friedrich, 1936 (excerpt) StA Munich

Prisoners marching through Dachau on their way to work, 1933 or 1934 Illegally taken photo, KZ-Gst. Dachau

Hans Cramer, mayor of Dachau, to the district administration, regarding a transport link with the Dachau concentration camp, July 13, 1937 (excerpt) StadtA Dachau

The administrative command of the SS training camp requested a regular transport link between the city and the concentration camp. The city administration supported this project for economic reasons. A bus line was introduced on November 22, 1937.

Prisoners in the Dachau Concentration Camp, 1933-1939

The first prisoners were German Communists and Social Democrats; later functionaries from parties of the political center were also imprisoned. From 1936 the proportion of Jewish and non-political prisoners increased considerably. The first foreigners were sent to the Dachau concentration camp in the wake of the occupation of Austria and the Bohemia territories.

Identity patches of the various prisoner groups in the Dachau concentration camp, around 1940 ITS

The groups across the top are:
• political, • professional criminal, • emigrant, • Jehovah´s Witness, • homosexual, • asocial.

Reading down:
• basic color, • badge for repeat offenders, • prisoners in punishment battalions, • badges for Jews, • special badges

Last group is divided into:
• Jewish racial violators (men who had sexual relations with "Aryan" women), • female racial violators ("Aryan" women in relationships with Jewish men), • escape risk, • prisoner number, • Pole, • Czech, • soldier in the German army, • prisoner 1a (prisoner foreman or "capo"); example

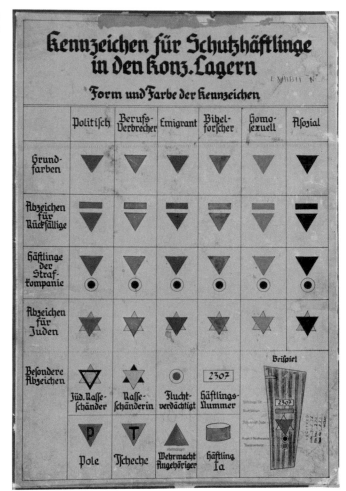

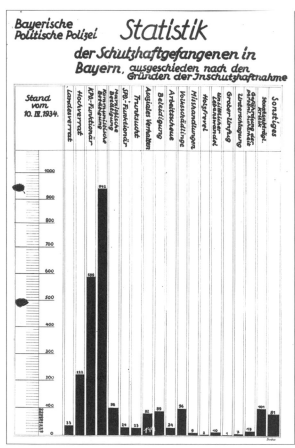

Bavarian Political Police statistics on the reasons for arrest of protective custody prisoners
Stand as of April 10, 1934 BayHStA

Prisoners in the Dachau concentration camp according to reasons for arrest, 1933-1938 (based on Gestapo data) BayHStA

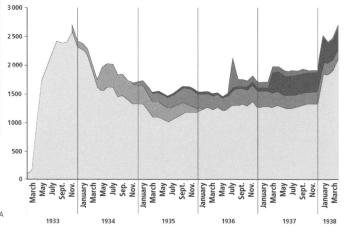

Protective custody
"Work-shy"
"Forced labor"
"Professional crimin…
"Operation beggar"

Beginning in 1933, a large number of political party members affiliated with the workers' movement and the trade unions, as well as some individual liberal and conservative opponents of Nazism were sent to the concentration camps. Many of them had already served regular prison sentences for their resistance activities.

Political prisoners in the Dachau concentration camp, May 24, 1933 Photo: SS, BA Ludwigsburg

Josef Mörtel
(1915-1998)
Together with his father and brother, Josef Mörtel, a member of the Socialist Workers' Youth in Weiden, smuggled illegal Social Democratic publications from Czechoslovakia into Bavaria. In May 1934 all three were arrested and given prison sentences. After serving their sentences, they were sent to the Dachau concentration camp. Their father, Franz Mörtel, died in April 1935. Josef Mörtel was made "camp runner" (Lagerläufer). Whereas his brother Franz was released in April 1939, Josef was first permitted to leave Dachau in April 1941. In 1943, Josef Mörtel was conscripted into the "probation battalion 999", a penal unit of the German army. In Greece he deserted and joined the partisans. After the war he became chief of police in Weiden. Photo: Josef Mörtel, 1941, private ownership

Protective custody order issued by the Secret State Police (Gestapo) against August Baumann, March 25, 1938

Many political opponents were sent to concentration camps after serving their regular prison sentences.
KZ-Gst. Dachau

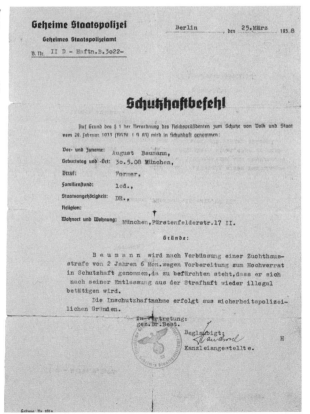

Emil Meier (b. 1909)
A Communist party official, Emil Meier was among the first prisoners sent to the Dachau concentration camp in March 1933. He was first released on April 26, 1935. In April 1937 the Gestapo brought him, along with thirty other communists from Munich, back to Dachau for a few weeks. He was arrested by the Gestapo for the third time in December 1944 for producing and spreading illegal fliers. In February 1945 he was imprisoned in the bunker of the Dachau concentration camp for a short time. AMA

Ludwig Göhring (1910-1999)
A member of the Communist Youth League in Nuremberg, Göhring was arrested for illegal activities in the summer of 1933. In the Dachau concentration camp he went through 14 horrific months in the bunker. Göhring spent more than eleven years in prison, nine of them in Dachau. In the fall of 1944 he was conscripted into the SS Dirlewanger brigade (a prisoner combat unit). Photo: private

Hans Adlhoch (1884-1945)
Workers' secretary of the Christian trade unions in Augsburg and Reichstag deputy for the Catholic Bavarian People's Party, Hans Adlhoch was arrested a number of times for his political opposition, beginning in 1933. Completely exhausted from the strenuous death march of April 1945, he died just a few days after liberation. Photo: around 1930, HdBG

Kurt Schumacher (1895-1952)
A steadfast opponent of National Socialism, the SPD Reichstag deputy was arrested in July 1933 and via the concentration camp at Oberer Kuhberg sent to Dachau. Here he gathered together a circle of dependable Social Democrats. Released in March 1943, he was rearrested and sent to the Neuengamme concentration camp from August to September 1944. After the war Schumacher became the first chairman of the re-founded Social Democratic party. Police records dept., AdsD, Seliger-Archiv

Those persons imprisoned in the concentration camps as "asocials" were primarily beggars, vagrants, alcoholics, prostitutes, Sinti and Roma, the so-called work-shy, idlers and those regarded as non-conformists. From the arrest operations carried out throughout the Reich in 1938, known as the "Aso Operation" and "Work-shy Reich", only men capable of work were to be sent to the concentration camps.

Herbert F. (b. 1913) The unemployed spinning mill laborer without permanent domicile was convicted of begging and vagrancy several times. In July 1936 he was detained as part of an arrest operation against beggars and sent to the Dachau concentration camp. In mid-August 1936, he was then committed to the Wanderhof, an institution for homeless people, in Herzogsägmühle near Schongau. Police records dept. StA Munich

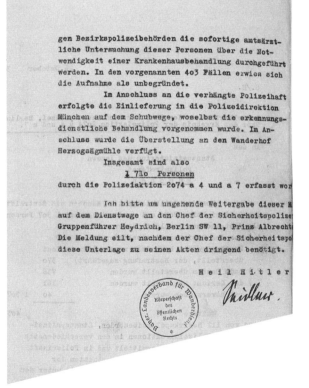

Report submitted to the Bavarian Ministry of Interior-Police Department on the arrest operation against beggars in July 1936, dated October 26, 1936
BayHStA

Members of the banned Jehovah's Witness organization refused to give the Hitler salute and serve in the military. At the Dachau concentration camp they were imprisoned in the punishment barrack up until 1939.
As the camp was cleared for rebuilding, they (144 prisoners) were transferred to Mauthausen, where many of them were murdered. Eighty-five Jehovah's Witnesses were dispersed throughout the Dachau subcamps at liberation.

Johannes Gärtner (1906-1940)
As a "serious bible student" Johannes Gärtner from Zwingenberg had refused to give the Hitler salute. He was sent to the Dachau concentration camp in June 1937. Together with the other

members of the Jehovah's Witness he was transferred to Mauthausen in September 1939. Completely exhausted and emaciated, he was sent back to Dachau in February 1940, where he died on April 26. WGZJ

They were patient without artifice and it was not uncommon that they shared the little food they had with a hungrier prisoner. Their faith, which could not be shaken, enabled them to endure with an utter scorn for death the terrible harassment that the SS subjected them to.

Hübsch, Island of Military Law (Insel des Standrechts); Hübsch was a prisoner in the Dachau concentration camp, 1937-1945.

The Jehovah's Witnesses were respected by their fellow prisoners for their honorableness and bravery.

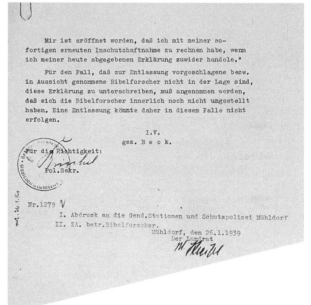

Letter from the Munich state police office on the conditions for release of Jehovah's Witnesses, January 23, 1939
Because the continuing terror against the Jehovah's Witnesses failed to have an impact, and because they themselves made no effort to escape and were hard-working, the SS deployed them in work details that were difficult to guard. StA Munich

From 1934 to 1939 over 200 homosexuals or persons denounced as homosexual were sent to the Dachau concentration camp – by the end of the war the total was at least 600. They were singled out for special harassment by the SS.

Leopold Obermayer (1892-1943) The Jewish wine merchant from Würzburg was imprisoned for homosexual tendencies in the Dachau concentration camp from January 1935 to December 1936, nine months of which he spent in the bunker. In December 1936, the Würzburg district court sentenced him to ten years imprisonment. At the end of 1942 he was transferred to Mauthausen for "extermination through work" because of his Jewish ancestry. He died there on February 22, 1943.
Police records dept., StA Würzburg

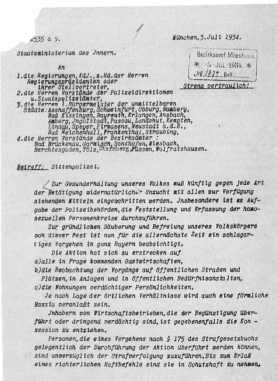

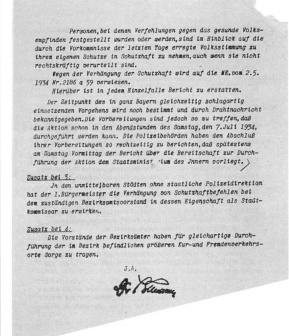

Order for an arrest operation against homosexuals issued by the Bavarian Interior Minister Adolf Wagner, July 3, 1934   IfZ

As of January 1935, the Bavarian police were able to take into "preventive custody" anyone with a previous criminal conviction and send them to a concentration camp. The SS used these persons to counterbalance the influence of political prisoners in running camp affairs. In the camps established from 1937 onwards, they were placed in the leading prisoner posts and played an integral role in creating the murderous conditions. At Dachau the political prisoners retained the majority of these posts until liberation.

Lorenz K. (b. 1901) The baker Lorenz K. had served in the French Foreign Legion from 1920 to 1925. By 1937 he had eighteen convictions for embezzlement, fraud and theft. In May 1937, he was taken into preventive custody and sent to the Dachau concentration camp. In June 1938 he was transferred to Flossenbürg. He was released in December 1940. Photo: Police records dept. StA Würzburg

The Reichsführer SS
and Chief of the German Police
in the Reich Ministry of the Interior
S-Kr. 3 No. 34/37 – g –

Berlin, SW, 2.23.1937

Urgent memo!

To the
State Criminal Police
Prussian Criminal Police Office
in Berlin

It is irrefutable that a reduction of criminality has been achieved through the German Criminal Police measures borne by the National Socialist spirit. But in many areas of the Reich criminals are still making their presence felt, spreading grave unease among the population through robberies, systematic burglaries and serious sexual offences. Their crimes indicate that they are acting not only due to an asocial attitude, but are motivated by hostility towards the state.

To prevent further crimes wherever possible, based on § 1 of the Reich President's Decree for the Protection of People and State from 2.28.1933 (RGBl. 1 p.83), I order that some 2,000 professional and habitual criminals or dangerous sexual criminals be taken into police preventive custody.

I authorize the Prussian Criminal Police Office with the carrying out of this measure. From the named dangerous sexual offenders and professional and habitual criminals presented to me by the Criminal Police offices, I demand that 2,000 be selected, arrested on a single day throughout the Reich and placed in concentration camps. I also order that the Inspector of the Concentration Camps be contacted promptly. When selecting the criminals to be taken into preventive custody, it is to be seen to that fathers with families are only then to be taken into preventive police custody if they represent a serious danger to the Volk community.

If complaints are raised against these measures, decisions are to be made after careful review. I will decide definitively on any further complaints.

Previously issued orders on police preventive custody and planned surveillance are not affected by these measures.

Report on the execution of these preventive measures is to be filed with me immediately.

Order issued by the Reichsführer SS and Chief of the German Police for an arrest operation against persons with previous convictions, February 23, 1937. Around 300 persons with previous convictions were sent to the Dachau concentration camp as a result of this order. IfZ

Not all German emigrants succeeded in settling abroad. Some were refused entry or expelled, while others believed that the danger of persecution had passed. In 1935, the Reich Ministry of the Interior ordered that returning emigrants be arrested and sent to the Dachau concentration camp. On May 1, 1935, there were 85 emigrants in the camp.

Herbert H. (b. 1921) Herbert H. tried to escape the threat of growing anti-Semitism by fleeing to the Netherlands. As a foreigner without financial means, he was deported back to Germany. Arrested at the border in January 1937, he was first sent to Sachsenhausen and then Dachau, before being transferred to the Buchenwald concentration camp. Released in July 1939, he successfully immigrated to Haiti a year later. Photos: Police records dept, 1937, NwHStA Düsseldorf

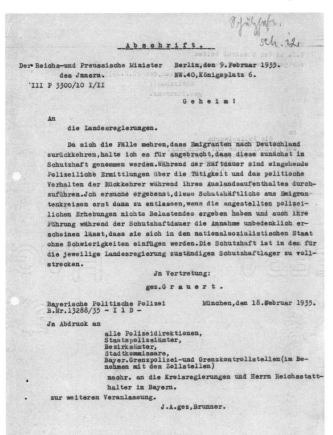

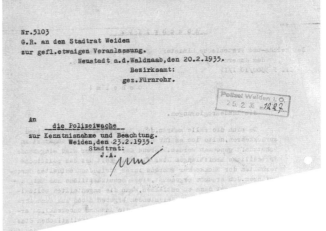

Decree of the Reich Ministry of the Interior on placing returning emigrants in concentration camps, February 9, 1935. BayHStA

On March 13, 1938, German troops occupied Austria, in October 1938 the border regions of Czechoslovakia, and on March 15, 1939, Bohemia and Moravia. Mass deportations to the concentration camps followed shortly afterwards

Austrian Prisoners

The first transports with prominent political opponents from Austria arrived at the Dachau concentration camp as early as the beginning of April 1938. SS men accompanying the deportations subjected them to brutal abuse.

Well-known Austrian personalities in the Dachau concentration camp included:

Robert Danneberg (1885-1942)
The lawyer Robert Danneberg, a prominent member of the Austrian Social Democrats, was head of the financial department in Vienna from 1932 to 1934. He was arrested in March 1938 and sent to the Dachau concentration camp on April 2. Later he was sent to the Buchenwald concentration camp and in 1942, because of his Jewish ancestry, to Auschwitz. He died there on December 12, 1942. VGAb

Maximilian Hohenberg (1902-1962)
Ernst Hohenberg (1904-1964)
The sons of Franz Ferdinand, the Austrian heir to the throne who was murdered in Sarajevo in 1914.
Photo: SV, the 1920s

Richard Schmitz (1885-1954)
Mayor of Vienna, 1934-1938. ÖNB

After the occupation of the Czechoslovakian border areas, a wave of terror was launched, primarily targeting Sudeten German Communists and Social Democrats. Around 2,000 persons were deported to the Dachau concentration camp.

Political opponents being taken away in Grundtal, around October 1938
Nazi propaganda postcard AdsD, Seliger-Archiv

Alois Ullmann (1888-1957) was a leading Sudeten German Social Democrat and co-founder of the Republican Defense movement. AdsD, Seliger-Archiv

Czech Hostages from Kladno 4.11

As a reprisal for the shooting of a German policeman, a group of 109 people from the political and public life of the Czech city of Kladno were brought to the Dachau concentration camp on June 16, 1939, via Špilberk castle and the Mauthausen concentration camp. Two of them did not survive the deportation, while two others arrived with fractured bones.

František Pavel (1869-1939) The 70-year-old mayor of Kladno committed suicide at Špilberk castle in unconfirmed circumstances, allegedly by jumping from the third floor. SUAP

From 1933 onwards anti-Semitism was a state ideology and government program. The National Socialists forced the exclusion, discrimination and persecution of Jewish citizens. The initial goal was to expel Jewish citizens from Germany. The means used became more radical over the years, ranging from boycotting Jewish businesses and the dismissal of Jews from the civil service in 1933 through to the adoption of the Nuremberg Laws in 1935 and the pogrom of November 9, 1938, after which around 11,000 Jews were deported to the Dachau concentration camp.

Pilloried The Jewish lawyer Michael Siegel was driven through the Neuhauser and Kaufinger Streets in Munich on March 10, 1933, with his trouser legs cut off, without shoes, and with a sign "I will never again complain to the police". Siegel had approached the police to help a client taken into protective custody. Photo: Heinrich Sanden (the writing on the sign has been retouched), SV

Burning synagogue in Essen, on November 9, 1938 Gst. Alte Synagoge

In Baden-Baden the arrested Jews were led through the city to the synagogue before they were taken away to the Dachau concentration camp in the evening, November 10, 1938
Photo: Josef Friedrich Coeppicus, StadtA Baden-Baden

In the first months of Nazi rule, mainly politically prominent Jewish persons were imprisoned in the concentration camps. They were classified according to the prisoner category "Jew" irrespective of the reason for their arrest. Placed into the penal company, they were subjected to inhumane tyranny and brutality.

> The government would never tolerate that someone be subjected to persecution only because they are a Jew.
>
> Hermann Göring at a reception for representatives of the foreign press, on March 25, 1933.

Jewish prisoners pulling the road-roller, July 20, 1938   Photo: SS, BA Ludwigsburg

Bruno Bettelheim (1903-1990)
The psychologist Bruno Bettelheim was sent to Dachau on a transport of Jews from Vienna in June 1938 and from there to the Buchenwald concentration camp. He was released in April 1939 and immigrated to the United States. His book "The Informed Heart. Autonomy in a Mass Age" (1960) ranks as one of the literary classics about the concentration camps. SV

Roll call at the Dachau concentration camp, end of November 1938 Painting by David Ludwig Bloch, 1940
The painter and graphic artist David Ludwig Bloch was arrested after the "Reichskristallnacht". He remained imprisoned in the Dachau concentration camp till the middle of December 1938. In April 1940 he succeeded in immigrating to Shanghai. There he painted this picture. KZ-Gst. Dachau

The Jews were hounded, chased, beaten, pushed, kicked and abused with rifle butts. … Stretchers came and to our horror the climax was to now be reached: they were in the meantime unloading the dead! Actually one has to say: those murdered during the journey!

Account on the arrival of one of the large transports of Austrian Jews in June 1938
Hübsch, Island of Military Law (Insel des Standrechts), manuscript, KZ-Gst. Dachau

Penal company, July 1938 Jewish prisoners pull a transport wagon, known as the "moor express".
Photo: SS, BA Ludwigsburg

Like the Jews, Sinti and Roma were also persecuted by the Nazi regime. Subjected to the Nuremberg Racial Laws of 1935, they were forced into guarded internment camps in many places. In 1938-1939 numerous Sinti and Roma were arrested and deported to the concentration camps.

"Gypsy camp" in Düsseldorf-Höherwerk, 1937
BA Koblenz

Interrogation of Josef G. in Cologne.
The "racial hygienists" forced those questioned to give particulars on kinship relations for the drawing up of family trees and the categorization as "gypsy". BA Koblenz

Foreign blood is all blood that is neither German blood nor related to German blood. Of foreign blood in Europe are regularly only Jews and gypsies. Those of foreign blood do not receive the rights of Reich citizens in principle.

Wilhelm Stuckart/Hans Globke, commentary on the German Racial Laws, 1936 (excerpt)

The commentary borrows formulations used in decrees and statements issued by Reich Minister of the Interior Frick in 1935-1936.

On June 28, 1939, some 550 Austrian Sinti and Roma were deported to the Dachau concentration camp. Many of them were put to work cultivating the "plantation". After the temporary closure of the camp in September 1939, they were sent to the Buchenwald and Mauthausen concentration camps. Only a few survived the murderous work in the quarries there.

The Sinto Baptist Winterstein Photo: BA Ludwigsburg

Stefan Sarközi (on the right with the bass) with his band from Unterschützen/Burgenland.
DZ Sinti and Roma, Heidelberg

A group of Roma from the Burgenland, July 20, 1938 Photo: SS, BA Ludwigsburg

The Dachau Concentration Camp under SS Command

The living conditions of the prisoners worsened dramatically when the SS took command of the Dachau concentration camp in April 1933. In June 1933 the second camp commandant, Theodor Eicke, began developing a concept for SS rule over the camp that became the model implemented in all concentration camps up to the end of the war.

SS guard company at an inspection by the leader of the German Labor Front, Robert Ley, May 1936
BA Ludwigsburg

Founded in 1925, the "protection squad" (Schutzstaffel, or SS) of the NSDAP was placed under the leadership of Heinrich Himmler in 1929. After the Nazi takeover of power in 1933, the SS developed into a central institution of surveillance, persecution and terror. Its rapid rise began in 1934, following the assassination of SA leader Ernst Röhm, known as the Röhm Putsch. With the founding of the "Inspectorate for the Concentration Camps" in 1934, Himmler fostered the centralization of the concentration camps under SS leadership. After he was appointed "Chief of German Police" in June 1936, he controlled the entire police apparatus. In 1939 Himmler then merged the leadership levels of the Secret State Police (Gestapo), the Criminal Police and the Security Service (SD) of the SS into the Main Office of Reich Security (RSHA).

Heinrich Himmler and Hitler's deputy Rudolf Hess visiting the Dachau concentration camp, May 1936   Photo: SS, BA Ludwigsburg

Heinrich Himmler (1900-1945) Heinrich Himmler, national leader (Reichsführer) of the SS since 1929, became the chief of police in Munich and political police commander in Bavaria in 1933. As early as 1934 he was appointed inspector of the Prussian Secret State Police and political police commander for all states (Länder). By 1936 Himmler was in charge of the entire police force. In 1943 Hitler appointed him Reich Minister of the Interior and after the unsuccessful assassination attempt of July 20, 1944, to the post of commander of the Reserve Army. Himmler was one of the top officials responsible for the persecution of political opponents in Germany and the occupied territories. He was also one of those chiefly responsible for the murder of millions of European Jews. He committed suicide after his arrest in May 1945.

Heinrich Himmler (left) with Theodor Eicke, who had been commandant of the Dachau concentration camp in 1933-1934, around 1941-1942
Photo: SS, BA Koblenz

On October 1, 1933, Eicke issued camp regulations. He also introduced a new administrative structure and decisively shaped the training received by the SS at Dachau, which indoctrinated recruits with an utter disdain for human life. When he was appointed inspector of the concentration camps in 1934, Eicke applied the Dachau regulations to all the existing and newly established camps.

Theodor Eicke (third from right) as inspector of the concentration camps, in the Lichtenburg concentration camp, March 1936 Photo: SS, USHMM

Theodor Eicke
(1892-1943)
Eicke became commandant of the Dachau concentration camp in June 1933. From 1934 to 1939 he was head inspector of all concentration camps. In November 1939 he became lieutenant general in the Waffen-SS (weapon-SS) and commander of the SS "Death's Head" division, which was responsible for guarding the concentration camps. Eicke died on February 26, 1943, in an airplane crash. Photo: SS files, BA Berlin

The Dachau camp regulations of October 1933 were a brutal punishment code for prisoners and detailed duty regulations for the SS guard units. The rigorous rules aimed at breaking the will and personality of the prisoners and preventing escape attempts.

Disciplinary and punishment regulations for the prisoner camp, October 1, 1933 (excerpt)
Unlike the camp regulations of other earlier concentration camps, which corresponded to usual prison rules, the Dachau disciplinary and punishment regulations contained instructions for corporal punishment and executions. StA Nuremberg

Copy
Dachau concentration camp, 10.1.1933
Camp headquarters
Disciplinary and punishment regulations for the prisoner camp
...
§ 6.
Punished with 8 days of s t r i c t d e t e n - t i o n a n d 2 5 b l o w s at both the beginning and end of the detention will be:
1.) whoever makes disparaging or mocking remarks to SS members, intentionally refrains from the prescribed attestations of respect, or through other conduct shows that he will not obey the obligations of discipline and order.
...
§ 8.
Punished with 14 days of s t r i c t d e t e n - t i o n a n d 2 5 b l o w s at the beginning and end of the detention will be:
1.) whoever leaves or enters the prisoner camp without escort, whoever joins without authorization a work column that is marching out,
2.) whoever makes derisive remarks in letters or other communications about National Socialist leaders, the state and government, its authorities and institutions , or whoever glorifies Marxist or liberal leaders or the November parties, or tells of occurrences in the concentration camp,
3.) whoever keeps banned objects, tools, weapons for hacking or stabbing in his barrack or in straw sacks.
...
§ 11.
Whoever in the camp, at the workplace, in the barracks, in the kitchens and workshops, lavatories and rest-places politicizes with the aim of s e d i t i o n , holds inflammatory speeches, meets with others for this purpose and forms cliques; or whoever roams around, gathers true or untrue reports with the aim of aiding enemy horror propaganda about the concentration camp or its institutions, or collects, receives, hides, passes or hands them on to outside visitors or others, smuggles them out from the camp, sends them with released or transferred prisoners in writing or verbally, hides them in clothing or other objects, or uses stones etc to throw them over the camp wall, or draws up secret notes; or further, whoever climbs onto barrack roofs or trees with the aim of inciting sedition, sends signals or seeks outside contact by flashing lights or other means; or whoever encourages others to escape or commit a crime, and for this purpose offers advice or support through other means, they shall be h a n g e d a s a r e b e l on the basis of revolutionary law!
§ 12.
Whoever physically assaults a guard or a SS man, or refuses to obey orders or perform work at the workplace, calls on or encourages others to act the same with the aim of inciting sedition, leaves a marching column or a work site as an insurgent, or calls on others to do the same, whoever during the march or at work yells, screams, agitates or holds an address, they shall be s h o t on the spot or later hanged as an i n s u r g e n t .
...
§ 19.
Detention will be enforced in a cell, fitted with a hard plank, with bread and water. The prisoner receives a warm meal every fourth day. Punishment includes heavy manual or particularly dirty labor, to be performed under special supervision. As additional penalties the following come into consideration:
Punishment exercise drills, beatings, mail ban, deprival of meals, hard bedding, pole hanging, reprimand and warning.
All punishments will be entered into prison records.
...

Concentration camp commandant,
Eicke
SS-Oberführer

**Carrying out of corporal punishment
in the Dachau concentration camp on
December 24, 1938**
Drawing by Albert Kerner, 1945-46, KZ-Gst. Dachau

Dachau concentration camp   10.1.1933
Camp headquarters

D u t y   r e g u l a t i o n s

for escorts and prison guards

pp. [gap in original document]

6. Guard duty

Whoever allows a prisoner to escape will be
arrested and handed over to the Bavarian
Political Police due to negligent freeing of a
prisoner.

If a prisoner attempts to escape, then he is to
be shot at without warning. No guard who has
shot an escaping prisoner in the execution of
his duties will be punished.

If a guard is physically assaulted by a prisoner,
then the assault is not to be countered with
physical force, but solely with the use of firearms.
Any guard who does not observe this regulation
must expect instant dismissal. Whoever ensures
cover will rarely need to expect a physical
assault.

If a prisoner group rebels or revolts, then it is to
be shot by all guards on duty. Warning shots are
prohibited.

The working hours are set by the camp commandant. Whoever allows prisoners to file in early
is guilty of gross breach of escort duty and can
be dismissed.

When a work troop must cease work early for
some reason, then the troop leader must
have the reason for this affirmed on the reverse
side of the duty sheet by the construction
section or the office in charge.

Commandant of the concentration camp,

Eicke

SS-Oberführer

**Directive issued by Theodor Eicke, commandant of the Dachau concentration camp, dealing
with regulations for escorting and guarding prisoners,** October 1, 1933 StA Nuremberg

Organizational Structure of the Dachau Concentration Camp

In 1933-1934 Theodor Eicke introduced a tightly structured administrative organization. With this he created the prerequisites for the complete regimentation, repression and exploitation of the prisoners. The commandant's staff was organized into five sections:

the commandant's headquarters and the attached offices of the adjutant, the political division, the prisoner camp direction, the administrative leadership, the medical division headed by the camp doctor.

The commandant's staff and, in particular, the SS barrack leaders strongly influenced the nature of the tyrannical rule in the camp. Appointed and controlled by the SS, and hence dependant on the SS, the prisoner functionaries took on important administrative tasks and disciplinary responsibilities in the barracks and the work details.

Organizational structure of the Dachau concentration camp, 1933-1934

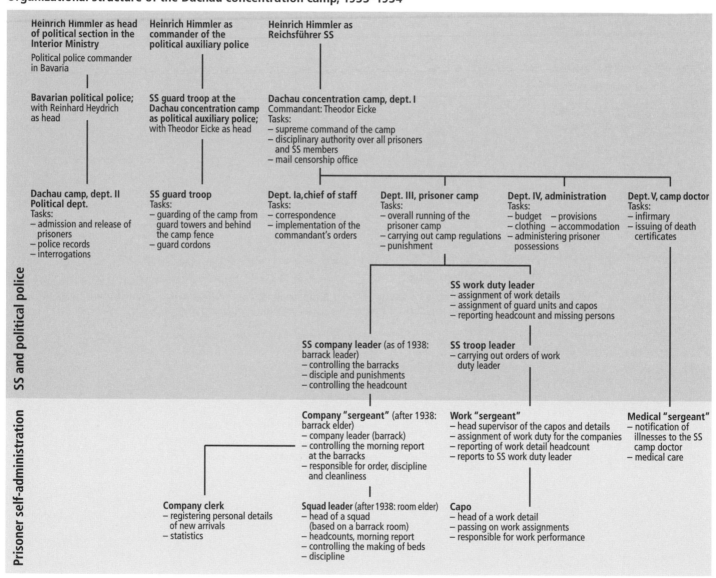

Tuchel, Inspektion; KZ-Gst. Dachau

Located adjacent to the prisoner camp was the garrison area, where the SS leaders and guard troops were ideologically and militarily drilled. Anti-Semitism, racism and hatred of all political opponents were the basic tenets of this training. In the first years, SS members of other concentration camps also underwent this "school of violence".

SS Death's Head divisions marching through Dachau, undated Photo: SS, BA-MA

SS leadership school of the Dachau concentration camp, around 1937 Photo: SS, BA Berlin

Theodor Eicke (second from left) with SS guards at a social gathering, 1934
Photo: SS, Hugh Taylor Collection, London

Theodor Eicke presents the Death's Head regiment "Upper Bavaria" to Hitler at the Nuremberg Reich Party Congress, 1937 Photo: SS, BA-MA

When commandant Theodor Eicke was informed that reports were allegedly to be smuggled out of the camp, he had the grounds dug up where the tin can containing them was allegedly buried. He had brutal punishments meted out to all Jewish prisoners, and four prisoners were murdered in the bunker. All prisoners were prohibited from gaining release and receiving mail and newspapers until the end of 1933.

> …a punishment drill was carried out till we lost our senses. Lie down – stand up – run – march – march – fall down – crawl – roll – no, not here you pig-Jew – through this puddle here – that's the way…drink you dog, the puddle water here! …– here over the wooden wall – roll – sing – that's how it went through sand and dirt, over undergrowth, over wooden beams, logs, ditches, spring boards, for hours on end! The elderly, the sick and the weak collapsed. Burkhard, Just Dance Jew

Wilhelm Franz (1909-1933)
The Munich KPD functionary Wilhelm Franz was accused of having taken notes on the crimes in the camp and hiding them. He was murdered in the bunker. The SS passed off his death as a suicide. Photo: around 1930, KZ-Gst. Dachau

Martin Stiebel (1899-1934)
Martin Stiebel was exposed to exceptionally harsh humiliation and abuse by the SS as a Jew and Communist. On October 17, 1933, he was thrown into the bunker, where he was then found hanged in his cell on April 2, 1934, obviously murdered by the SS. Photo: from the 1920s, HdBG

Notification from the Dachau concentration camp on the ban on mail, November 18, 1933
KZ-Gst. Dachau

After the Nazi takeover of power in 1933, the SA wanted to strengthen its role within the Nazi state. It strove towards the formation of a people's army that was to replace the Reichswehr (the German Army). In contrast to Hitler, the SA leaders wanted a "second revolution". Using the pretense that the SA was planning a coup d'état, Hitler had Ernst Röhm, high-level SA functionaries, and political opponents shot on June 30 and July 1, 1934. Primarily carried out by the SS and extending throughout the Reich territories, this murder operation cost over one hundred persons their lives, twenty-one of them in the Dachau concentration camp. This signaled the rise of the SS. It became an independent organization of the Nazi Party and gained considerably more power.

Ernst Röhm, SA chief-of-staff (center), **and August Schneidhuber, police president of Munich** (second from left), with Adolf Hitler at the Reich Party Congress in Nuremberg, 1933 SV

Both Röhm and Schneidhuber were shot by Eicke and Michael Lippert, head of the Dachau guard troops.

Fritz Gerlich (1883-1934)
As publisher and editor-in-chief of the Catholic weekly "Illustrierter Sonntag" (as of 1932 "Der gerade Weg"), Fritz Gerlich strongly criticized Hitler and the Nazi movement. Members of the SA arrested Gerlich in the night of November 9-10, 1933. The publicist was severely mistreated. After a year in prison, he was taken to the Dachau concentration camp on June 30, 1934, and murdered there on the following day.
Photo: around 1930, SV

Walter Häbrich (1904-1934)
Walter Häbrich was chairman of the German Communist Youth League in 1928-1929. He started writing for the Munich KPD paper "Neue Zeitung" in 1930. After it was banned in 1933, Häbrich became a member of the illegal editorial office. On September 23, 1933 he was taken to the Dachau concentration camp, where he was shot dead on July 1, 1934. Photo: around 1925, KZ-Gst. Dachau

Gustav Ritter von Kahr (1882-1934)
Ritter von Kahr was president of the regional government in Upper Bavaria between 1917 and 1920, Bavarian prime-minister from 1920 to 1921, and state commissioner in 1923. Kahr ordered the Reichswehr and Bavarian police to quell the Hitler Putsch in 1923. In an act of revenge, he was murdered in 1934. Photo: from the 1920s, SV

After the Röhm Putsch, all of the concentration camps were taken over by the SS and placed under the authority of Theodor Eicke, who in the meantime had been appointed to the post of inspector of concentration camps. Eicke reorganized all of the concentration camps on the Dachau model. The smaller camps were closed down, and the only camps remaining in June 1935 were Dachau, Lichtenburg, Sachsenburg, Esterwegen, and the women's camp at Moringen.

Illegal flier with the text of the camp regulations for the Lichtenburg concentration camp, December 1935 BA, Berlin

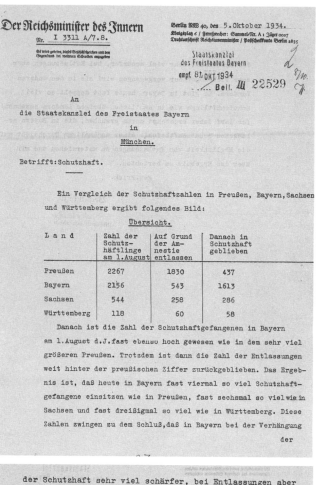

Letter from Wilhelm Frick, Reich Minister of the Interior, to the Bavarian state chancellery, listing the number of protective custody prisoners, October 5, 1934. BayHStA

From 1934 onwards, when establishing new concentration camps Theodor Eicke utilized his post as inspector of the concentration camps to deliberately appoint those SS leaders and guard troops who had received their training at Dachau. These SS leaders ensured that the "Dachau model" was then applied at the other camps. They occupied key positions, developed a tightly meshed network of connections, and influenced personnel appointments.

"Career paths" of the Dachau SS personnel

Hans Aumeier	1934-1938	Camp leader Flossenbürg concentration camp, 1938-1941 Camp leader Auschwitz concentration camp, 1942-1943 Commandant Vaivara concentration camp, 1944
Richard Baer	1933-1934	Adjutant Neuengamme concentration camp, 1942-1943 Economic and Administrative Main Office, 1942-1943 Commandant Auschwitz concentration camp, 1944-1945 Commandant Mittelbau-Dora concentration camp, 1945
Karl Fritzsch	1934-1940	Camp leader Auschwitz concentration camp, 1940-1941 Camp leader Flossenbürg concentration camp, 1942-1944
Rudolf Höß	1934-1938	Camp leader and adjutant Sachsenhausen concentration camp, 1938-1940 Commandant Auschwitz concentration camp, 1940-1943 Section chief in Economic and Administration Main Office, 1942-1943
Franz Hofmann	1933-1942	Camp leader Auschwitz concentration camp, 1942-1944 Camp leader Natzweiler concentration camp, 1944
Max Koegel	1933-1936	Adjutant Berlin Columbia House concentration camp, 1936 Adjutant Dachau concentration camp, 1937-1938 Commandant Lichtenburg concentration camp, 1938-1939 Commandant Ravensbrück concentration camp, 1939-1942 Commandant Majdanek concentration camp, 1942-1943 Commandant Flossenbürg concentration camp, 1943-1945
Hans Loritz	1933-1934	Commandant Esterwegen concentration camp, 1934-1936 Commandant Dachau concentration camp, 1936-1939 Commandant Sachsenhausen concentration camp, 1940-1942
Günther Tamaschke	1933-1934	Deputy to the inspector of the concentration camps, 1935-1936 Commandant Lichtenburg concentration camp, 1937-1938
Franz Xaver Trenkle	1933-1938	Deputy camp leader Dachau concentration camp, 1942-1944 Camp leader Bergen-Belsen concentration camp, 1944
Martin Weiss	1933-1940	Commandant Neuengamme concentration camp, 1940-1942 Commandant Dachau concentration camp, 1942-1943 Commandant Majdanek, 1943-1944

Up until the war began, Heinrich Himmler personally appointed the commandants of the Dachau concentration camp. Heinrich Deubel, in this position since December 1934, seemed especially suited for this office as an "old party fighter". But he soon gained the reputation of being too lenient towards the prisoners. His successor, the notorious commandant of the Esterwegen concentration camp, Hans Loritz, arrived in April 1936. The prisoners experienced his command as one of the worst phases they had to endure in the camp's history. The change of commandants was not in any way incidental, but was closely connected to the extension of the concentration camp system.

Heinrich Deubel (far right) and Oswald Pohl (far left), administrative chief at the SS Main Office, accompany Robert Ley (center), head of the German Labor Front, on an inspection, February 11, 1936 (detail) Photo: SS files, BA Ludwigsburg

Heinrich Deubel
(1890-1962)

Deubel was appointed commandant of the Dachau concentration camp in December 1934. His leadership style was, however, too lenient for the SS. Moreover, Deubel had attracted unwanted public attention for his unauthorized assumption of authority, misappropriation, and excesses. He was therefore transferred in April 1936 to the post of commandant at the Berlin Columbia House concentration camp. After that camp was closed down, Deubel went back to work as a customs official in 1937. He was interned from 1945 to 1948. The criminal proceedings against him for his involvement in National Socialist crimes were eventually dropped. Photo: SS files, BA Berlin

Hans Loritz (1895-1946)

Hans Loritz joined the SS and the NSDAP in 1930. In 1933-1934 he worked in the SS offices located on the grounds of the Dachau concentration camp and had close contact to the commandant, Theodor Eicke. Loritz took over the post of commandant at the Esterwegen concentration camp in Emsland (between Hanover and the Dutch border) in July 1934. In 1936 he took over leadership of the Dachau concentration camp. He ordered the SS guard units to treat the prisoners with extreme brutality. The unbridled excesses improved his standing with the inspector of the concentration camps, Theodor Eicke. In December 1939 Loritz became commandant of the Sachsenhausen concentration camp. In September 1942 he was made commander of the concentration camps that were to be set up in Norway. After the end of the war, in 1946, he committed suicide in the Neumünster internment camp. Photo: SS, BA Berlin

Between 1933 and 1939, 35,000 prisoners were incarcerated, most of whom were subsequently released. Over 500 prisoners died.

During the first years the terror unleashed by the SS on individual prisoners completely dominated the everyday life and routine in the camp. With the rise in prisoner numbers, entire prisoner groups increasingly became victims of SS assaults. The SS placed the lives of the prisoners under total control and strict regimentation.

Roll call in November 1938, drawing by Karl Freund (1938-1939 in the Dachau concentration camp), December 17, 1938 KZ-Gst. Dachau

Prisoners at roll call
The prisoners had to line up mornings and evenings on the roll-call area to be counted. Irrespective of the weather, they were forced to stand at attention. This torture could drag on for hours.
Photo: SS, "Münchner Illustrierte Presse", July 16, 1933, BaySB

Daily routine

Summer:

4 am	Reveille
5.15 am	Roll call
6 am - midday	Work
Midday - 1 pm	Break (including exit and entrance march)
1 pm - 6.30 pm	Work
7 pm	Roll call (lasts approx. 1 hour)
8.45 pm	"Everyone in bed"
9 pm	"Everyone in bed"/ "Lights out"

Winter:

5 am	Reveille

Working hours: from daybreak to nightfall

Daily routine of the prisoners as of 1938, recorded by Otto Kohlhofer (prisoner in the Dachau concentration camp, 1938-1945), in the mid-1960s

In the initial phase of the camp, work often served the purpose of humiliating and tormenting the prisoners by making them perform senseless activities. Within the camp different workshops were soon set up that were put under the direct command of the commandant. One section of the prisoners was responsible for the maintenance and servicing of the camp, while others worked outside the concentration camp grounds in so-called external work details guarded by the SS. As the camp was enlarged and extended in 1938, the prisoners were forced to work for weeks on end without a rest day and frequently even at a running pace. A systematic expansion of the SS companies was launched in 1938. This significantly increased the importance of the prisoners' labor for the SS.

"The Dachau Sand Pile" Painting by Herbert Appelbaum (1937-1938 in the Dachau concentration camp), oil on canvas, 72 x 84 cm, 1959
Gift of Ruth Appelbaum, Yad Vashem Art Museum Collection, Jerusalem

Prisoner hammering nails, July 20, 1938
Photo: SS, BA Ludwigsburg

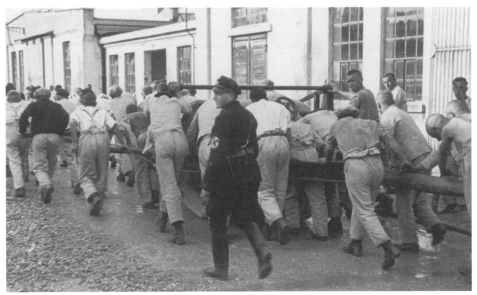

Prisoners during road-leveling work on the camp grounds, May 24, 1933
Photo: SS, BA Ludwigsburg

In the first years of the camp, the prisoners were not yet forced to go hungry. The food was, however, monotonous, deficient in vitamins and of little caloric value. The prisoners were able to have money transferred to them. With this they could then purchase a limited amount of food in the camp canteen at exorbitant prices. In the first months some prisoners still wore civilian clothes. The remaining prisoners were issued overalls made of canvas material as normally used in prisons and detention centers.

Prisoners during the issuing of food at the first camp, May 24, 1933 Photo: SS, BA Ludwigsburg

Prisoner in the striped uniform, June 28, 1938 (detail) Photo: SS, BA Ludwigsburg

Prisoners with food pails on the way from the kitchen to the barracks, June 28, 1938 Photo: SS, BA Ludwigsburg

Until 1938 the prisoners lived in ten stone barracks belonging to the former munitions factory. Every barrack had five dormitory rooms, each of which housed 54 prisoners. In summer 1938, the 34 barracks of the new camp were completed. The prisoners were allocated 30 barracks which were called "blocks". Every one of these housing barracks was comprised of four rooms, known as "Stuben", which included a day room and a dormitory. For every two "Stuben" there was a common wash and toilet facility. Fifty-two prisoners were housed in each "Stube", giving a total of 208 prisoners in each barrack. The entire camp was planned to house more than 6,000 prisoners.

Stone barracks, 1933   Photo: SS, BA Ludwigsburg

Interior view of a barrack, 1933   Photo: SS, "Münchner Illustrierte Presse", July 16, 1933

Dormitory, as of 1938   Photo: SS, NIO

The "Dachauer Zeitung" reports: "The political prisoners listen to the orders given by the SA", 1933
Photo: SS, "Dachauer Zeitung", June 26, 1933

Functionary prisoners. The SS camp command transferred a significant share of supervisory and organizational tasks in the prisoner camp to selected prisoners. The SS granted these prisoners certain privileges and hoped to turn them into informers and accomplices to their crimes. At the same time, these prisoners received a share in the unbridled power of the SS. Political prisoners chiefly occupied these posts in the Dachau concentration camp. In most cases they strove to help their fellow prisoners. In the years prior to the war there were only a few functionary prisoners who participated in the crimes committed by the SS.

The medical care provided for the prisoners was inadequate from the very beginning. The protective custody camp leader decided whether a prisoner was ill and permitted to visit the camp SS doctor. As a rule, the SS doctors were not concerned with restoring a prisoner to health.

> When in retrospect I try to find a general principle for how the medical services were conducted in the concentration camps, I can only locate one: the more prisoners die, the better.
>
> Adam, Night over Germany; Walter Adam was in the Dachau concentration camp, 1938-1943.

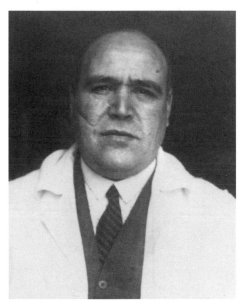

Delwin Katz (1887-1933)
The Nuremberg doctor Delwin Katz was in double jeopardy as a Jew and Communist. At first he provided medical care for ill and injured fellow prisoners during official duty, at times also in secret. He was murdered on October 18, 1933.
StadtA Nuremberg

Prisoner examination form for the admission of Walter Neff, March 14, 1938 KZ-Gst. Dachau

In the first years of the camp there were periodic releases, including larger groups of prisoners. Those released had to report daily to the police where they lived.

Release from the Dachau concentration camp by Commandant Theodor Eicke, Christmas 1933 SV

400 Schußhäftlinge werden aus dem Dachauer Lager entlassen

Aus Anlaß des überwältigenden Sieges des Nationalismus am 12. November und des herannahenden Weihnachtsfriedens hat der polit. Polizeikommandeur Bayerns eine Entlassung von über 500 Schußhaftgefangenen in ganz Bayern verfügt. Aus dem Konzentrationslager Dachau werden etwa 400 Schußhäftlinge entlassen. Grundsätzlich werden nur solche Schußgefangene entlassen, die sich bisher einwandfrei geführt haben und von denen zu erwarten ist, daß sie sich wieder als nützliche Mitglieder der Volksgemeinschaft erweisen werden.

Press article from the "Amper-Bote" on releases from the Dachau concentration camp, December 9, 1933

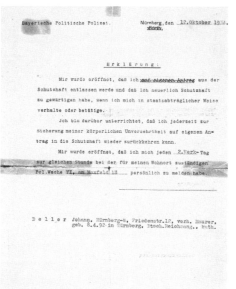

Release certificate for the prisoner **Johann Deller,** 1934 KZ-Gst. Dachau

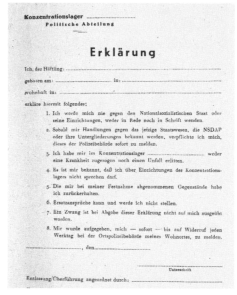

Sworn statement to remain silent by the prisoner **Johann Deller,** October 12, 1934. This declaration had to be signed by all prisoners prior to their release. KZ-Gst. Dachau

The prisoners lived in constant fear of terror and assaults by the SS guards. The "Disciplinary and Punishment Regulations for the Prisoner Camp", in effect in the Dachau concentration camp from October 1, 1933, and later also applied in the other concentration camps, merely feigned an ordered punishment system. In reality it lay in the hands of any SS man to file arbitrary reports that lead to punishment. An individual prisoner, but also an entire group of prisoners, could be punished at any time. The most frequently used methods included beatings, the so-called tree or pole hanging, and standing at attention. There was individual and collective denial of meals as well as detention in the camp prison. Besides the punishments set out in the camp regulations, various torments and torture methods were inflicted on the prisoners, and they were also threatened with the death penalty.

Standing at attention on the roll-call area as punishment, June 28, 1933   Photo: SS, BA Ludwigsburg

Copy
Dachau concentration camp, 10.1.1933
Camp headquarters
Discipline and punishment regulations for the prisoner camp
Introduction
    Within the framework of the existing camp regulations, the following punishment regulations will be enacted to maintain discipline and order for the area of the Dachau concentration camp. All prisoners of the Dachau concentration camp are subjected to these regulations from the time of their entering the camp to the hour of their release.
    The executing penal authority lies in the hands of the camp commandant, who is personally responsible to the Political Police commander for the carrying out of these adopted camp regulations.
    Tolerance means weakness. Knowing this, there will be ruthless intervention wherever it appears necessary in the interest of the Fatherland. The decent, goaded Volk comrade will not be affected by these punishment regulations. Let it be said to the political agitators and intellectual inciters – of any orientation –, you better not get caught, otherwise we shall go for your throats and, following your own recipe, silence you.

"On the Pole", drawing by Anselm Grand, prisoner in the Dachau concentration camp, 1939-1941.   Grand, Turm A ohne Neuigkeit!, 1946

Disciplinary and punishment regulations for the prisoner camp, October 1, 1933 (excerpt)
StA N

View along the corridor of the camp prison (bunker) after liberation, around May 1945
NA, Washington

Open resistance by the prisoners was not possible against the superior strength of the SS guards. From the very beginning, however, they developed diverse forms of self-assertion and secret ways of offering one another help and support. Again and again they were successful in smuggling news out of the camp. Although the exchange of letters with relatives and friends was strictly censored, it was just as significant for their psychological balance as was the effort they put into maintaining personal hygiene and engaging in intellectual activities in the short period of spare time. A camp library, staffed by prisoners, was set up as early as fall 1933.

Camp library, as of 1938 Under the guidance of the SPD politician Kurt Schumacher, the library became a secret center of political discussion and a place for illegal meetings of Social Democratic prisoners. Thanks to the ignorance of many of the SS men, the prisoners were able to smuggle in books banned in National Socialist Germany. Photo: SS, 1941, NIO

Greeting card sent by Hans Kaltenbacher from the Dachau concentration camp on Mother's Day, undated KZ-Gst. Dachau

Rolf Cavael (1898-1997)
The painter Rolf Cavael was imprisoned in the Dachau concentration camp from December 1936 to April 1937 for publicly demonstrating his anti-Nazi attitude. Photo: Fotoarchiv Timpe, BaySB

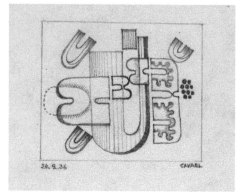

Drawing by Rolf Cavael
Rolf Cavael was forced to draw architectural plans for the SS. This enabled him to secretly procure paper and create a series of pencil drawings that he then managed to smuggle out upon his release. KZ-Gst. Dachau

Hans Beimler (1895 - 1936)
Hans Beimler was elected Reichstag deputy for the Communists in July 1932. He was arrested in Munich on April 11, 1933, and committed to the Dachau concentration camp on April 25, 1933. On May 9, 1933, he managed to escape, fleeing via Czechoslovakia, to the Soviet Union, where he wrote an account of his camp experiences, entitled "Im Mörderlager Dachau" (In the Murder-Camp Dachau). From mid-1935 to mid-1936 he was in Switzerland. From there he was involved in organizing Communist resistance in southern Germany as a leading functionary. From 1936 he fought in the Spanish Civil War as a member of an International Brigade. Hans Beimler died on December 1, 1936.

Hans Beimler Photo: BaySB

Hans Beimler, Four Weeks in the Hands of Hitler's Hell-Hounds, 1933
The first account of conditions in the Dachau concentration camp was published in Moscow under the German title "Im Mörderlager Dachau". An English version was published in London the same year. Photo: BaySB

Aus dem Dachauer Konzentrationslager
Kommunist Beimler entflohen — 100 Mark Belohnung auf seine Wiederergreifung ausgesetzt.

In der Nacht zum gestrigen Dienstag ist der bekannte Kommunistenführer und ehemalige Reichstagsabgeordnete, Schlosser Hans Beimler aus Augsburg, aus dem Konzentrationslager Dachau entflohen. Der Flüchtling, der bisher noch nicht wieder ergriffen werden konnte, trug eine braune Knickerbockerhose und eine braune Joppe. Er war glatt rasiert und trug kurzgeschorene Haare. Ein besonderes Kennzeichen sind seine auffallend großen und weit abstehenden Ohren.

Für Angaben, die zur Ergreifung des Entflohenen beitragen können, ist von der Lagerverwaltung eine Belohnung von 100 RM. ausgesetzt. Beimler war jener Kommunistenführer, der kurz vor der nationalen Revolution in einer Versammlung im Zirkus Krone den Ausspruch getan hatte: „Bei Dachau sehen wir uns wieder!" Anscheinend war er von der Wiedersehensfeier in Dachau nicht erbaut.

*

Report in the "Amper-Bote" on Hans Beimler's escape from the Dachau concentration camp in May 1933, May 11, 1933
As it was almost impossible to escape from the concentration camp, the successful attempt by the Communist Reichstag deputy Hans Beimler was regarded as a sensation.

Although the number of deaths was comparatively low in the first years, every prisoner nevertheless still lived under the constant fear of death. Some prisoners committed suicide because they could no longer endure this ever present threat and the constant abuse and mistreatment. Prisoners were often driven to suicide or "shot while trying to escape" by the SS guards. The murder of a concentration camp prisoner was frequently declared to be suicide.

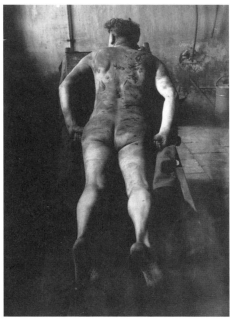

Judicial post-mortem of the murdered Louis Schloss (1880-1933), May 17, 1933
The Nuremberg businessman Louis Schloss died as a result of mistreatment on May 16, 1933, in a prison cell of the Dachau concentration camp. To feign a suicide he was subsequently hung up on a hook with suspenders. Photo: StA Munich

Fünfzig Ermordete in Dachau

London, 3. Jänner. (Inpreß.) Der „Manchester Guardian" berichtet über das Konzentrationslager in Dachau:

Die 2200 bis 2400 Internierten sind in zehn Baracken untergebracht. Unter ihnen sind ungefähr 50 Intellektuelle, einige Angehörige der Mittelschichten, 50 oder 60 Nazi, etwa 500 Sozialdemokraten, 2 Offiziere, mehrere Kriminelle, 15 Ausländer; alle andern sind Kommunisten. Die weitaus größte Zahl der Gefangenen besteht aus Arbeitern.

Die Internierten sind in zehn Kompanien zu maximal 270 Personen gegliedert. Die siebente Kompanie ist die „Disziplinarkompanie", die erste ist gebildet aus sozialdemokratischen und kommunistischen Arbeitern, die zweite aus Juden.

Die kommunistischen Funktionäre, die sich weigern, den Nazi politische Informationen zu liefern, werden in Zellen eingeschlossen. Die Zellen sind feucht, dunkel und nicht geheizt. Die Ketten, an denen die Strafgefangenen gefesselt sind, sind eingemauert. Das Nachtlager besteht aus einfachen Holzbrettern. Im September wurden die Internierten gezwungen, 21 neue Zellen zu bauen.

In Dachau wird die Strafe der körperlichen Züchtigung angewandt. Die Gefangenen werden mit drahtumwickelten Ochsenziemern geschlagen, die sie selbst verfertigen müssen. Sie erhalten 25 bis 75 schwere Schläge.

Kommunisten und Sozialdemokraten werden grundlos bei der Ankunft im Lager geschlagen. Man schlägt die Gefangenen auch mit feuchten Handtüchern. Sieben SA.-Männer, die am 1. August ins Lager eingeliefert wurden, sind derart mißhandelt worden, daß zwei von ihnen, Amuschel und Handschuch, starben. Der Kommunist Fritz Schaper wurde so zugerichtet, daß er sich zwei Monate lang nicht bewegen konnte. Am 2. September zerschlug ein Naziwächter einem Gefangenen mit einem Faustschlag den Unterkiefer.

Die Inhaftierten werden auch oft mit brennenden Zigaretten verbrannt.

Unter den am furchtbarsten Mißhandelten sind L. Buchmann, Georg Freischütz und der Journalist Ewald Thunig. Der Münchener Kommunist Sepp Götz wurde ermordet, nachdem er so mißhandelt worden war, daß er sich nicht mehr aufrichten konnte. Der Student Wickelmeier wurde durch einen Schuß getötet. Der Kommunist Fritz Dressel wurde zu Tode mißhandelt.

Getötet wurden der Stadtrat Hausmann, Lehrburger, der Reichsbannermann Aron, Willi Franz, Buerk, ein kommunistischer Funktionär aus Memingen — insgesamt fast fünfzig Männer.

Der Korrespondent des „Manchester Guardian" ist im Besitz der Namen von neun Aufsehern, die die Gefangenen mißhandeln und morden.

"Fifty Murdered in Dachau". Report in the Viennese newspaper "Arbeiter-Zeitung" on January 4, 1934

"The autopsy was not able to prove death by hanging."

Conclusion drawn by the court commission protocol of the Dachau municipal court after the autopsy and post-mortem of Louis Schloss, May 17, 1933 (excerpt) SA Nuremberg

Deaths in the Dachau concentration camp, 1933-1939

Year	Deaths	Year	Deaths
1933	22	1937	41
1934	33	1938	256
1935	12	1939	183
1936	11		

Based on the entries of the registry offices Prittlbach and Dachau as well as additional sources (state of research as of 2002)

The Dachau Concentration Camp during the Period of Germany's Military Conquests, 1939-1942

The National Socialists exploited the state of war to perfect their hold over the life and death of the prisoners. The concentration camps became sites for exterminating the leading strata of the conquered nations. The murder operations reached their peak after the attack on the Soviet Union in June 1941.

The National Socialists exploited the state of war to extend their rule over the life and death of the prisoners.

There will be no releasing of prisoners from protective custody for the duration of the war...

Decree issued by Reinhard Heydrich, chief of the Security Police and the Security Service (SD), October 24, 1939 (excerpt)

Allgemeine Erlass-Sammlung, RSHA 2 F VIII a, BA Berlin RD 19/3

The tightening of protective custody

On order of the Reichsführer SS and Chief of the German Police, all protective custody prisoners to be transferred to a concentration camp during the war are to be assigned a special penal section...

Aside from deciding on the committal to a concentration camp, the Reichsführer SS and Chief of the German Police will also order that beatings be given in individual cases.

Guidelines issued by the Main Office of Reich Security on October 26, 1939 IMT XXVII Doc. 1531-PS

"Special treatment" (execution without trial)

...in the submission to the Reichsführer SS, the state police office reports shall not be repeated line for line, word for word, but formulated briefly in one's own words (as much like a telegram as possible).

Guidelines issued by the Secret State Police (Gestapo) office on September 26, 1939

IMT Doc. NO-905

Through "special treatment" the SS leadership secured for itself the right to impose death sentences. The decision was made solely on the basis of a short submission to Himmler.

35746	Lauterbach Wilhelm	20.5.02	Streitshau	[illegible]	Nürnberg
35747	Rauwolf Anton	10.11.08	Augsburg	[illegible]	[illegible]
35748	Schmidt Rudolf	11.12.12	Coburg	Gärtner	Coburg
35749	Neubauer Willi	31.5.07	Neustadt b. Coburg	Drucker	Neustadt b. Coburg
35750	Wannengiesser Nikolaus	21.1.71	St. Wendel-Saar	Schreiner	St. Wendel Saar
35751	Jelinski Alexander	19.9.21	Kamion	Maler-Lehrling	Kamien
35752	[illegible] Wladislaw	16.9.19	Górka	Schmied	Zalesie
35753	[illegible] Friedrich	21.2.21	Krom	H. Arbeiter	[illegible]
35754	Kettner Alfons	17.7.21	Podgórz	-"-	[illegible]
35755	Mandhey Franz	16.1.21	Wolsko	Schuster	[illegible]
35756	Schmolke Johann	5.5.21	Popiten	Hütten-Arbeiter	Inowroclaw
35757	Kasrath Zbigniew	22.7.20	Cirkowo	Landarbeiter	Cirkowo
35758	Czajka Andreas	2.2.19	Trzeszinowo	Student	Nakel
35759	Lauter Franz	4.4.12	Pokrent	Friseur	Inowroclaw
35760	Rabenda Boleslaw	31.5.12	Thorn	Hilfsarbeiter	Thorn
35761	Maruschak Boleslaw	15.2.19	Wielowies	-"-	Thorn
35762	Jelinski Johann	24.6.89	[illegible]	Träger	Kamin
35763	Matern Franz	24.6.07	Allenstein	Schmied	Vitkau
35764	Gorczynski [illegible]	17.8.11	Czarnikau	Fleischer	Czarnikau
35765	Koniczkowska [illegible]	14.7.04	Thorn	[illegible]	Thorn
35766	[illegible]	14.4.20	Inowroclaw	-"-	Inowroclaw
35767	Milan Johann	6.8.11	[illegible]	[illegible]	Hohensalza
35768	Osinski Wladislaw	10.4.06	Hohensalza	[illegible]	Hohensalza
35769	Tabolski Franz	3.3.00	Wandsburg	Händler	Wandsburg
35770	Bilski Peter	25.11.87	[illegible]	Landwirt	[illegible]
35771	Wiadern Johann	6.3.09	Wysoka	-"-	[illegible]
35772	Vitomski Josef	19.12.08	Ostrowite	Landarbeiter	Ostrowite
35773	Kubski Stanislaus	13.8.76	Ksiens	Pfarrer	Hohensalza
35774	Juresik Josef	6.1.12	Wiszyn, Berent	[illegible]	Konarzyn
35775	Libocki Johann	23.1.74	Kempa	[illegible]	Deutsch-Walde

Admissions register of the Dachau concentration camp,
September 21, 1939
NA Washington

On September 10, 1939, 551 prominent Czech citizens were taken hostage and deported to the Dachau concentration camp. The first 99 Poles followed shortly after; the SS called them "snipers" and treated them appallingly. During the temporary vacating of the camp, the Czechs and Poles were transferred to the Buchenwald concentration camp, where the Poles were murdered as "snipers".

Josef Čapek (1887-1945), one of the Czech hostages; the popular painter and journalist was the brother of the famous writer Karel Čapek.
Photo: the 1930s, Gst. Buchenwald

At the end of September 1939, the Dachau prisoner camp was vacated and used as a training facility for the SS Death's Head division. The Dachau prisoners were distributed amongst the Buchenwald, Flossenbürg and Mauthausen concentration camps. In spring 1940, the political prisoners who had survived were transferred back from Mauthausen and Flossenbürg.

Waiting for the serving of meals in the Flossenbürg concentration camp
Photo: SS, KZ-Gst. Dachau

Newly arrived prisoners on the roll-call area of the Buchenwald concentration camp, 1939
Photo: SS, USHMM

The "stairway of death" in the quarry of the Mauthausen concentration camp Photo: SS, NIO

The worsening of the living conditions after the start of the war led to the rapid physical and psychological decline of the prisoners. The number of deaths reached monstrous dimensions.

Increase in deaths in the Dachau concentration camp after the start of the war

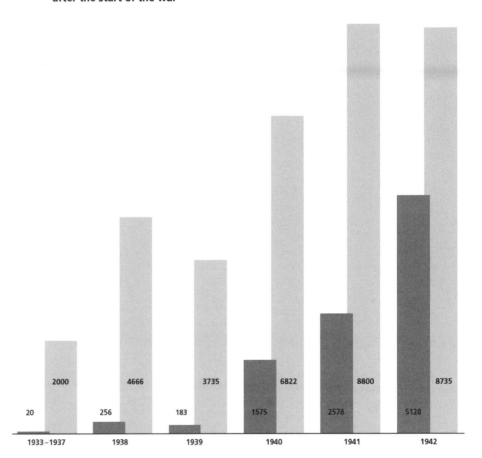

1933–1937	1938	1939	1940	1941	1942
2000	4666	3735	6822	8800	8735
20	256	183	1575	2578	5128

Registered deaths
Based on figures from the registry offices Prittlbach, Dachau and Dachau II (the figures are not exhaustive since numerous deaths were not registered); the numbers for the years 1933-1937 show the yearly total; the numbers for 1942 also include the prisoners murdered at the "euthanasia" facility in Hartheim.

Average number of prisoners
The figures for the years 1938-1939 are marked by the high number of Jewish prisoners deported in connection with the annexation of Austria and the November pogrom.

Extermination through work

The prisoners were driven on by the SS and the capos until they were completely exhausted. The worst conditions at the Dachau concentration camp were mostly in the gravel pit, at the construction sites of the SS garages, and on a property belonging to the "plantation" that was yet to be fenced in, which was called "Freiland II".

Murderous excesses on the "plantation"
At the carp pond, which had just been dug and still held very little water, prisoners were held so long in the water, with their head down while their legs were raised backward, till they drowned.
Grand, Tower A without any News; Anselm Grand was in the Dachau concentration camp, 1939-1941

Shot "while attempting to escape" was almost a daily occurrence on the "Freiland II plantation" in the spring of 1941. The dead person here is the Jewish prisoner Abraham Borenstein, shot on May 15, 1941. Photo: SS, KZ-Gst. Dachau

The roller with a human team on the "planta-tion", drawing by the Czech prisoner Karel Frinta, 1941; Frinta was in the Dachau concentration camp in 1940-1941 and again from 1942 to 1945.
KZ-Gst. Dachau

Returning from the "plantation", drawing by Hans Quaeck, 1955; Quaeck was in the Dachau concentration camp, 1941-1945.
KZ-Gst. Dachau

The completely exhausted prisoners were granted no rest in the barracks. The short period of time free from work was spent "making beds", cleaning dishes and lockers, and scrubbing the floor. All these harassing cleaning tasks were accompanied by mistreatment and enforced by draconian punishments.

"Making beds"

…the made bed had to be like the artwork of a master decorator…whoever's bed-making gave cause for complaint was reported for punishment. Everyone wanted to spend as long as possible making his bed, but this was technically impossible at the same time, especially since the beds were stacked on top of one another in three stories, so there erupted in the dormitory an awful struggle amongst the prisoners…
Feuerbach (pseudonym for Ferber), 55 Monate Dachau, 1945; Walter Ferber was in the Dachau concentration camp, 1938-1942

The wooden floor in the day room of a barrack had to shine like parquet.
The floorboards were scrubbed three times a day to a brilliant shine. The lockers were polished with "organized" sand-paper so that they appeared as if they had been planed down. The aluminum eating bowls and cups had to shine as if they were made of silver. Photo: SS, around 1941, NIO

Prisoners in the dormitory, drawing by an unknown prisoner Biskupski, Ksieza Polscy

After the start of the war, punishment was inflicted even more cruelly. Pole hanging and beatings became the "basic punishment". At the end of 1940, pole hanging was carried out in the baths, where up to 50 inmates were subjected to this torture at the same time.

These are the torments of hell! The whole body-weight hangs from the arms, whIch are twisted backwards. And the monsters stand in front of you and laugh at your pain, ask you whether you now want to confess, slap you in the face and pull and tug at your body. When you stay silent they swing you, often they whip you at the same time.
Edgar Kupfer-Koberwitz, Die Mächtigen und die Hilflosen; Kupfer-Koberwitz was in the Dachau concentration camp, 1940-1945.

During the real beatings "Herr" SS Hauptsturmführer Zill placed great value on the SS men using all their strength. But it was not allowed to proceed too quickly. Calmly smoking his cigarette, he repeated again and again: "Slowly, slowly, he's to thoroughly enjoy this!"
Julius Schätzle, Wir klagen an!, 1946; Schätzle was in the Dachau concentration camp, 1938-1944.

The beating, drawing by an unknown prisoner Najnigier, Powrot z daleka

"Pole hanging", drawing by an unknown prisoner Biskupski, Ksieza Polscy

The calorie content of the food rations lay far below the daily requirement. Although prisoners attempted to deaden the tormenting hunger by eating herbs, roots, potato peels and the like, they could not delay the physical decay accelerated by the permanent inadequacy of the food rations.

Dandelions

There are other things you can eat. First, there are the dandelions. You simply pull out the whole root, shake off the soil, and stick the whole thing in your mouth. Unfortunately there are only a few of them at our work site.

Jean Bernhard, Pfarrerblock 25487, 1962; Bernhard was in the Dachau concentration camp, 1941-1942

Drawing by Vlastimir Kopač, March 1945 KZ-Gst. Dachau

As a result of malnutrition, the prisoners suffered from tuberculosis, dysentery and phlegmon (infection of the cell tissue). The SS doctors undertook next to nothing to care for the ill. Doctors from the prisoner ranks were not permitted to work in the infirmary. The infirmary became a place of death.

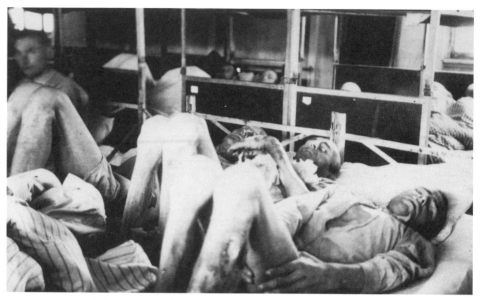

Phlegmon ward Phlegmon was a frequent and feared disease in the concentration camps. The starved prisoners suffered from famine edema. Their swollen legs were susceptible to injury and became easily infected. The wounds discharged pus and the tissue died.
Photo: taken after liberation and reproduced in: the notes of Karel Kašák, KZ-Gst. Dachau

Dental outpatient station, around 1941
The well-equipped dental outpatient station served as a propaganda showpiece. The main task of the personnel was actually to extract gold teeth from dead prisoners. Photo: SS, KZ-Gst. Dachau

Discovery of gold extracted from teeth at the Dachau concentration camp, 1945
Upon liberation US soldiers discovered gold from teeth that had been extracted from dead Dachau prisoners. Photo: US Army, NA Washington

Infirmary capo Josef Heiden (on the right; 1938-1941 in the Dachau concentration camp)
The political prisoner Josef Heiden ruled as infirmary capo until January 1942. Although he had no medical training, he operated on perfectly healthy prisoners. He was also involved in executions in the bunker as hangman. Photo: SS, NIO

In the wake of the territorial gains made by Germany's war of conquest, many new prisoner groups comprised of different nationalities were deported to the concentration camps. German prisoners were soon in the minority.

Committal of prisoners according to nationalities from the start of the war on September 1, 1939, to June 30, 1942, based on the admissions register. Many prisoners were transferred to other camps.
KZ-Gst. Dachau

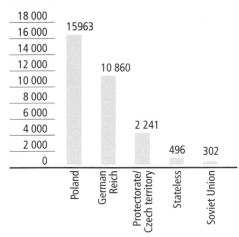

Nationality	Number
Poland	15963
German Reich	10 860
Protectorate/ Czech territory	2 241
Stateless	496
Soviet Union	302

A group of Polish prisoners after liberation, May 3, 1945   KZ-Gst. Dachau

Cover of the prisoner file on Raoul Roissard
Raoul Roissard was detained in February 1944 in Annecy during the arrest operation "spring wind". Via the Drancy camp, he was deported to the Dachau concentration camp in July 1944.
Główna Komisja Badania Zbrodni Przeciwko Narodowi Polskiemu, Warsaw

In 1940, 13,375 Poles were committed to the Dachau concentration camp, mainly from the new Reich territories ("Reichsgaue"), from where it was planned to "remove" seven to eight million Poles. Members from the leading strata of society were either murdered or deported to concentration camps. The remaining population was to be resettled in the "General Government" area of Poland.

> We must see to it that, at least in the provinces now belonging to Germany, the problem of the Polish minority is solved and exterminated in our time. The problem must be exterminated.
>
> Speech by Heinrich Himmler in front of Gauleiters and party functionaries on February 29, 1940 (excerpt) Himmler, Geheimreden.

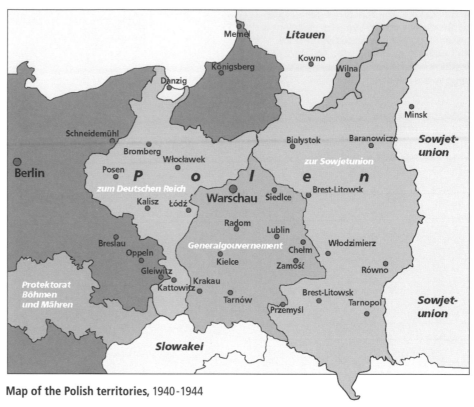

Map of the Polish territories, 1940-1944

Zygmunt Raźniewski (b. 1922)
Zygmunt Raźniewski belonged to the large group of Polish high school students deported to the concentration camps because they represented the coming generation of an undesirable educated stratum. Photo: 1950-1951, private ownership, HdBG

A group of Polish prisoners after liberation, May 3, 1945 KZ-Gst. Dachau

Deportation of the leading strata of Polish society
It has been decided that the leading stratum, which may not remain in Poland under any circumstances, is to be sent to German concentration camps, while for the lower strata provisional concentration camps are to be set up behind the special squads along the border, from where these strata are, if needed, to be deported to the rest of Poland.
Instruction issued by Reinhard Heydrich on the tasks of the security police while combat was still underway, September 7, 1939 (excerpt) Verfolgung, Hg. Kurt Pätzold.

After the start of the war, the persecution of the Jews was extended to the occupied territories and radicalized further. Jews were deported to ghettos. Their marking with the Star of David patch became obligatory. In the occupied areas of the Soviet Union, execution squads and the special task forces of the security police and the SD murdered a large part of the Jewish population. The murder of the European Jews had begun.

The yellow star KZ-Gst. Dachau

The shooting of Jewish women and children in Libau, Latvia 1941 BA Ludwigsburg

Jews from Würzburg being led away to a transport taking them to the ghettos in eastern Europe, 1942 StA Würzburg

In the Łódź ghetto, between 1940 and 1944
Photo: Walter Genewein, JM Frankfurt/Main

Jews from France in the Drancy camp prior to deportation, 1942 Żydowski Instytut Historyczny, Warsaw

The Jewish prisoners were isolated in the penal block. They were inhumanely harassed, humiliated and mistreated. Many were murdered. Between 1940 and 1942, over 1,500 Jews were deported to the Dachau concentration camp, almost 700 of whom died in the camp. In October 1942, all Jewish prisoners in Dachau were transported to Auschwitz.

Alleged suicide of a Jewish prisoner in the shed of the old crematorium, October 17, 1941
Photo: SS, KZ-Gst. Dachau

Admissions and departures register of the Dachau concentration camp. The deaths of four Jewish prisoners in detention ("KA" in the fourth column, above right) are entered on October 17, 1941. They were obviously prisoners murdered after having worked in the crematorium. KZ-Gst. Dachau

Max Jelonek (1883 - 1940)
The Jewish prisoner Max Jelonek was arrested in May 1940 for "spreading reports of atrocities". In June 1940 he was sent to the Dachau concentration camp, where he died just a few weeks later. Photo: Police records dept., NwHStA Düsseldorf

Crematorium work detail
As long as this "old crematorium" was exclusively in use, the prisoner detail working here comprised of a few Jews who did not sleep in their barrack, but were housed in two cells in the bunker. They were not to find any opportunity to talk about what went on in the crematorium… When the five or six Jews were completely worn out by this gruesome work, which often continued uninterrupted day and night, they were simply shot on the spot by their work detail leader.
Ludwig Schecher, Looking Back at Dachau, unpublished account; Schecher was in the Dachau concentration camp, 1935-1945 KZ-Gst. Dachau

In Bohemia and Moravia the same mass deportations as in Poland were not carried out, because the Nazis did not want to endanger production in the large Czech armaments industry. A total of some 5,500 Czechs were imprisoned in the Dachau concentration camp. At least 1,346 lost their lives.

Occupation policy in the "Protectorate of Bohemia and Moravia"
...the basic line must...remain unspoken, that this area must at some time become German, and that in the end the Czech has no business to be in this area...I thus require calm in this area so that the worker, the Czech worker for the German war effort, uses all his energy here, so that we do not delay...supplies from the giant stock of armaments industries existing here.
Inaugural speech given by Reinhard Heydrich as deputy head of the Reich Protectorate of Bohemia and Moravia in Prague, October 2, 1941 (excerpt)
Die Vergangenheit warnt, (ed.) Fremund and Král

Three generations of the Feierabend family in the Dachau concentration camp
Ladislav Feierabend was a minister in the Czechoslovakian exile government in London. On July 1, 1942, his family members still in the protectorate were arrested. The men were sent to the Dachau concentration camp, the women to Ravensbrück.

Professor Karel Feierabend (1861-1945)
Father of the minister in exile. Photo: private ownership

The Feierabend family (shortly before arrest)
From the left:
Vladimir Feierabend, nephew of the minister
Karel Feierabend, nephew of the minister
Marie Feierabendová, sister-in-law of the minister. Together with the minister's wife Hana, she was imprisoned in Ravensbrück.
Karel Feierabend, brother of the minister
KZ-Gst. Dachau

Miroslav Kubik was one of 84 high school pupils arrested on June 20, 1942, in Roudnice, in the middle of lessons, for harboring "hostile sentiments against the Reich". Kubik was deported to Dachau via Auschwitz. Photo: Police records dept. of the Auschwitz concentration camp, KZ-Gst. Dachau

After Germany's victory over France, the French Vichy government handed over most of the Spanish Civil War veterans who had been interned in camps in France to the German authorities. Five hundred were deported to the Dachau concentration camp. Due to their discipline and solidarity they were held in high regard by the other prisoners.

Hans Landauer (b. 1912) Hans Landauer was also among the Spanish Civil War fighters sent to Dachau. He had joined the International Brigade as a sixteen year old in 1937. He survived his time in the camp. Since his retirement, Hans Landauer has been active in the Documentation Archive for Austrian Resistance in Vienna. Photo: Police records of the Gestapo Vienna, 1941, DÖW

Hermann Langbein (1912-1995)
The Austrian communist Hermann Langbein was among those Spanish Civil War veterans sent to Dachau. In August 1942 he was transferred to Auschwitz, where he worked as a clerk in the prisoner administration. After the war he published several books on the concentration camps.
Photo: Police records of the Gestapo Vienna, 1941, DÖW

A total of 2,720 clergy were imprisoned in the Dachau concentration camp; 1,780 were Polish priests. After Vatican intervention, from March 1941 they received communion wine for mass and better provisions. A room in barrack 26 was set up for use as a chapel. In September 1941 these privileges were withdrawn; from now on only German priests were allowed to visit the chapel.

Monstrance used by the Polish priests
The original monstrance, made of tin from cans, is kept in a private museum in Głucha Puszcza near Poznań
Photo: Antoni Bryliński, private ownership, KZ-Gst. Dachau

The chapel Photo taken after liberation, April/May 1945, KZ-Gst. Dachau

The food carriers Beginning in the spring of 1941, the clergy were forced to perform this extremely arduous work for the whole camp.
Drawing: Petrovič, KZ-Gst. Dachau

Michał, Kozal, (1893-1943), a Polish bishop, died in the infirmary in January 1943. He was probably murdered by injection. Photo reproduced in Majdański, Zeugen.

Gabriel Piguet, (1887-1952), archbishop of Clermont/France, was transported to Dachau from the Natzweiler concentration camp in September 1944. Between January 1945 and the liberation of the camp he was detained in the bunker as a "special prisoner". Portrait by Ferdinand Dupuis, Dachau 1944, private ownership, copy held by the KZ-Gst. Dachau

On the "plantation" – where medicinal herbs and plants were cultivated – many prisoners were tortured to death or shot "while trying to escape", especially during the cultivation work of 1939-1941. Some of the other work details, for example in the greenhouses and affiliated buildings (the pepper mill, drying room and labs), offered better chances of survival.

Greenhouses belonging to the "plantation", 1941 Photo: SS, KZ-Gst. Dachau

Prisoner at work on the "plantation", 1941
Photo: SS, KZ-Gst. Dachau

Beatings, harassment, death
They dragged a half-dead Jew to the plantation ... Here Capo Max Schnell beat him with the truncheon, urged him to hurry up, and heaped him with such insults that, in the whole world, could only be formed in the language of this country [Germany]. And so we marched. At the head of the column the Jews sang: let us sing and be gay ... That Jew died the following day. Journal entry by Karel Kašák.

There were numerous other work details besides the "plantation". The most arduous assignments were the gravel pit, the garage construction, and various building and earthmoving work. The prisoners regarded the work details in the workshops as relatively bearable. There are no SS photos of the arduous work details.

Prisoners at work in the armory workshop, probably 1942 Photo: SS, KZ-Gst. Dachau

Metalworking shop of the German Equipment Works (DAW) Photo: SS 1941, KZ-Gst. Dachau

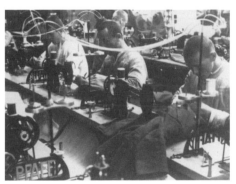

Tailoring work detail, 1941 Photo: SS, NIO

Angora breeding work detail, 1941 Photo: SS, KZ-Gst. Dachau

Under the brutal living conditions prevailing between 1940 and 1942, self-assertion and solidarity were of extreme importance for survival. Using the hours after lights out for talking about the military situation and holding modest cultural events gave many prisoners the resolve and strength to endure. The mutual help provided was often lifesaving.

The camp, drawing by an unknown prisoner, undated Private ownership

The drawing has the following dedication: "For Tadeusz Kulakowski, in remembrance of the camp, of walks taken together and of discussions on art, Dachau 1941"

Music in the tuberculosis section of the infirmary, drawing by Günther T. Turczynski, 1942; he was in the Dachau concentration camp, 1940-1943. KZ-Gst. Dachau

Money for impoverished prisoners

... for the Dachau prisoners returning from Flossenbürg, who were completely impoverished, transfers [were] undertaken so that the Dachau prisoners could sign over sums from their accounts to other comrades. This action was betrayed, and following an order by Zill [protective custody camp leader] the entire work detail, including Mursch [SS detail leader], was sent to the bunker, where we stayed for 45 days in the dark in solitary confinement, got something warm to eat only every 4th day, and everyone of us was whipped and received 25 double lashes, and we were then subsequently sent to the penal block for a year.

Evidence given by Ludwig Soswinski (1938-1944 in the Dachau concentration camp) in the preliminary proceedings against the former protective custody camp leader Egon Zill, September 22, 1950 (excerpt) StA Munich

The Austrian communist Ludwig Soswinski, capo of the "Schubraum paymaster office", used this post to organize the assistance action. DÖW

Card, drawn by Georg Tauber September 15, 1942; he was in the Dachau concentration camp, 1938-1945. KZ-Gst. Dachau

With the mass deportations of foreign prisoners to German concentration camps, beginning in 1940, the number of deaths in the Dachau concentration camp rose dramatically. Death became an everyday event. Dying was deprived of all piety and sympathy, and the dead were robbed of their dignity.

Death from starvation

In Dachau death only seldom had a heroic character. Death was something normal, it occurred everywhere: at roll call, at work, on the block road, at the toilets. In normal life the death of a cat that has died on the street draws attention and arouses pity. The emaciated, wretched prisoner lying in death attracted no great attention.

Zámečník, That was Dachau

Josef Stessel, shot "while trying to escape" on August 11, 1940 Photo: SS, KZ-Gst. Dachau

Franz Rabanda, died in the electrified fence on May 29, 1940 Photo: SS, KZ-Gst. Dachau

"Burial in Dachau", drawing by Karel Frinta; he was in the Dachau concentration camp 1940-1941 and 1942-1945. KZ-Gst. Dachau

After the start of the war, the concentration camp system was expanded. New camps were established. The number of prisoners rose from 21,400 as the war began in September 1939 to around 88,000 in December 1942.

The Natzweiler concentration camp in the Vosges, opened in 1941. Postwar photo, KZ-Gst. Dachau

The Neuengamme concentration camp near Hamburg, in early 1940 it became an independent camp. KZ-Gst. Neuengamme

The concentration camp system and the new camps, 1939-1942

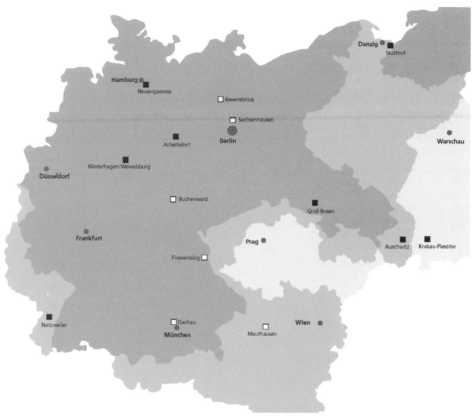

- ■ 1940-42 newly established concentration camps
- □ Concentration camps erected prior to 1940

- German Reich 1937
- Annexed territories
- Territories under German occupation

The Auschwitz concentration and extermination camp, established in 1940.
Muzeum Auschwitz-Birkenau, Oświęcim

The Stutthof concentration camp near Danzig (Gdansk), established 1942. KZ-Gst. Dachau

As early as 1941, the SS leadership began preparing for the expected rapid victory. In his capacity as "Reich Commissioner for the Strenghtening of Germandom", Heinrich Himmler planned to develop the conquered eastern territories for German settlement, exploiting the labor of the concentration camp prisoners. An enormous extension of the concentration camp system was planned for peacetime.

Fill up the camps with slaves

If we do not produce the bricks here, if we do not fill up our camps with slaves – in this room I express things very plainly and very clearly – with work slaves, who without any consideration of losses build our cities, our villages, our farmhouses, then after a war lasting years we will not have the money to produce settlements where real Germanic peoples can live and take root in the first generation.

Heinrich Himmler, address before an assembly of SS leaders, June 9, 1942 (excerpt)
Himmler, Geheimreden

"SS peacetime building program",
December 4, 1941
In his book The Slave State, published in 1981, the former armaments minister Albert Speer noted on the proposed amount for the construction of the planned concentration camps that:
"With 550 million Reichsmark 12,061 barracks could have been set up, which would have accommodated 4,016,000 prisoners." BA Berlin

---

II/3 -Allg.-55/Se./Lo.　　　　Berlin, 4.Dezember 1941

Vorläufiges Friedensbauprogramm des Hauptamtes Haushalt und Bauten, Amt II – Bauten.

1.) Waffen-SS
(Reichsgebiet +
Generalgouvernement +
Protektorat +
Skandinavien +
Niederlande)　　　　　RM　2.996.300.000,-
2.) KL Reichsgebiet　　　"　　550.000.000,-
3.) Polizei Reichsgebiet　"　　687.000.000,-
4.) Allgemeine SS　　　　"　　　88.000.000,-
5.) Sonderaufgaben
(Lazarett, Schulen, Verpflegs- und Bekleidungsanlagen,
Wohnungsbau für Waffen-SS,
Polizei und Allg.-SS)　"　2.656.055.000,-
6.) Neuer Ostraum
(für Waffen-SS, Polizei und
Sonderaufgaben zusammen)　"　6.098.730.000,-

vorläufige Gesamtsumme:　　RM　13.076.085.000,-

Aufgestellt:
Berlin, 4.Dezember 1941
Hauptamt Haushalt und Bauten
Amt II – Bauten

SS-Oberführer

Although "euthanasia" officially ceased on August 24, 1941, Himmler continued to use the lethal capacity of the facilities for the mass murder of concentration camp prisoners deemed no longer capable of work. The psychiatrists involved in the euthanasia program conducted the selection. The action ran under the codename "special treatment 14 f 13".

Doctors became murderers
The work is going so smoothly because the headings are already typed ... I eat in the camp; today at midday there was lentil soup with bacon in the mess, and then omelet for desert ... today after the meal we went for a walk ... In my bed I am sleeping extremely well ... Hopefully things are as good for you as they are for me; I feel splendid!"

Letter by Friedrich Mennecke from the Ravensbrück concentration camp, November 20, 1941 (excerpt), in Langbein, "…wir haben es getan", 1964.

With invented diagnoses doctors who had sworn the Hippocratic Oath sent hundreds of persons to their death each day. Mennecke viewed his activity as satisfying work.

Commemorative photo of the doctors' commission, September 3, 1941.
(From the right) The doctors Gerhard Wischer, Hermann Paul Nitsche, Friedrich Mennecke, Viktor Ratka, Rudolf Landauer (director of the "euthanasia" facility Hartheim near Linz) and the driver Erich Bauer
Sammlung Ernst Klee, Frankfurt/Main

The "euthanasia" facility at Hartheim castle near Linz. Here 2,674 prisoners from Dachau and several thousand from Mauthausen were murdered with poison gas. KZ-Gst. Dachau

In July 1941, Reinhard Heydrich ordered the deployment of special Gestapo squads in POW camps to select Soviet prisoners who were classified as "untenable" due to their Jewish ancestry, communist activities or other characteristics. They were then to be sent to the closest concentration camp for execution. At Dachau, the mass executions were carried out at the Hebertshausen shooting range.

Directives for "selecting" specific categories of Soviet prisoners of war for execution

It is above all necessary to find: all important functionaries of the state and the party, in particular professional revolutionaries, Comintern functionaries, all leading functionaries of the Communist Party of the Soviet Union and its subsidiary organizations in the central committees, the district and local committees, all peoples' commissars and their representatives, all former political commissars of the Red Army, the leading personalities of the central and intermediate instances in the state bureaucracy, the leading figures in the economic sector, the Soviet-Russian intelligentsia, all Jews, all persons who are deemed as rabble-rousers or fanatical communists.

Order No. 8, appendix 2, from Reinhard Heydrich, Chief of the Security Police and the Security Service (SD), July 17, 1941 (excerpt) StA Nuremberg

Reichsführer SS Heinrich Himmler, inspecting a camp holding Soviet prisoners of war, 1942 SV

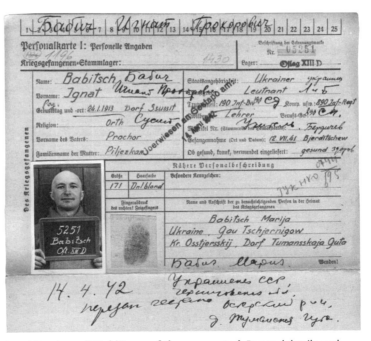

Ignat Prochorovič Babič, one of those executed. Personal details card from the POW camp, around March 1942. CA Podol'sk

Execution site for Soviet prisoners of war at the SS shooting range near Herbsthausen, April 1945

Photo: Karel Kašák with delayed-action shutter release, DZ Oberer Kuhberg

In 1941 an official "camp music detail" was formed. This group performed in front of the canteen during the frequent inspections of Nazi functionaries and foreign delegations. This was supposed to display the "excellent" conditions in the camp. "Camp music" also had to be played during the inflicting of torture so as to further humiliate the victims. On Sundays the group played for their fellow prisoners.

Camp music

If we succeeded … in creating from this camp music a carefree hour of forgetting for those buried alive behind the barbed wire, then even the most modest artistic achievement was a great deed in the improbable circumstances of the camp. The music always met with resounding applause from the thousands who not only filled the shower room but also the area in front of it. It was the most thankful and sincere applause musicians have ever received.

Kalmar, Zeit ohne Gnade

Camp choir made up of Czechoslovakian comrades
Ink drawing by Vladimír Matûjka, 1942.

The first semi-illegal choirs were formed between 1940 and 1942.

"Christmas singing of the nations"

One sacred music ceremony which I can never again experience on earth was the "Christmas singing of the nations". In the crammed chapel first the Italians sang a Christmas carol, then the Dutch, then the Luxembourgers. There then followed a very lively polyphonic French Noel choir, and then Czech and German choral singing. … But what has imprinted itself most in my memory was the polyphonic Polish Christmas chorus that had the form of a splendidly stylized polonaise.

Gregor Schwake (1944/45 in the Dachau concentration camp), on a Christmas celebration in the chapel of the priests' barrack.

Father Gregor Schwake composed many pieces of sacred music in the Dachau concentration camp, including the "Dachau Mass" for men's choir and brass instruments. It was first performed in the camp in September 1944.

Every written word was forbidden and the author risked being sent to the bunker or death…

Heiser, Mein Schatten in Dachau, (ed.) CID.

Henri Pouzol, born in 1914 in Jarnac, France, a teacher and writer, was arrested in 1942 and deported to the Sachsenhausen and Dachau concentration camps. From there he was sent to the Augsburg-Pfersee and Lauingen subcamps. He was liberated in the Dachau concentration camp at the end of 1945.

Mirco Giuseppe Camia (1925-1997)
Mirco Giuseppe Camia was arrested in Milan and deported to the Flossenbürg concentration camp. Via the Dachau concentration camp he was sent to the Kempten-Kottern subcamp in 1944. When he returned to Dachau in 1985 for the fortieth anniversary of liberation, he proposed the idea of creating the poetry collection "My Shadow in Dachau", with his own poems and the single poem of Nevio Vitelli, which he had carried with him for many years because it had made his return to life possible.

Mirco Camia as nineteen-year-old prisoner, 1944
Private ownership

My Shadow in Dachau

Mama, I'm not returning,
God has told me.

A hell without the feelings of the soul,
I've lived through it…

What have I done, Mama?
Do you know? Tell me
And kiss me in sleep,
Light and fleeting,
So that I'm not tempted to
Return the kiss
Like when you, leaning over me,
Cried for the rascal
…

Nevio Vitelli (1928-1948) was deported to the Dachau concentration camp in 1944, aged sixteen. He returned to Italy in 1945, where he died in 1948 from the effects of the deportation. Private ownership

The value of this poem

I met Nevio in the infirmary in Dachau where we laid in the same room … Both of us had deep inner wounds … he with his 17 years more so than I: behind us was the knowledge of things that we wanted to fight against but were unable to … there were the terrible memories with all the open wounds of the soul that no one could heal. Wounds deeper than the ones that weakened our bodies …

The value of this poem for me? …
It contains everything: the torment of captivity and the elegy of freedom, the memory of the greatest earthly love, maternal love … and something else that is banished from the normal thoughts of youth and from human suffering: forgiveness …

… it is not possible to endure subhuman conditions, to be nothing more than an "object" … without being pursued by it an entire lifetime, even in your soul, without destroying what you possessed before this experience –

… the beauty of a vision of the universe and mankind …

Nevio made it possible for me to find myself again in his unknown poem …

Mirco Camia (1944-45 in the Dachau concentration camp) on encountering Nevio Vitelli and his poem "My Shadow in Dachau", 1989. Heiser, Mein Schatten in Dachau, (ed.) CID

Aerial view of the Camp, 1945

Aerial photograph of the Dachau concentration camp, April 20, 1945
Luftbilddatenbank Ing. Büro Dr. Carls, Würzburg

1 Gatehouse (Jourhaus) with prisoners' camp entrance
2 Roll-call area
3 Service building
4 Bunker
5 Penal camp for the Waffen-SS and police
6 Camp road
7 Barracks (storage camp)
8 Camp museum, canteen
9 Labor deployment, Messerschmitt workshops
10 Prisoner living barracks (blocks 2-30)
11 Infirmary barrack A (outpatient ward, operating theatre)
12 Infirmary barrack B (clerk office, SS doctors, death chamber)
13 Infirmary and quarantine barracks (blocks 1-29)

14 Block 31: special barrack (brothel)
15 Disinfectory (for clothing)
16 Angora rabbit stalls
17 Camp market garden
20 Old crematorium
21 Large crematorium with gas chamber
25 Military armaments workshops
26 SS community center
27 Eicke Square
28 Living quarters for SS members
29 Restaurant, shop
30 Commandant's villa
31 SS access road
40 Sentry house/ SS camp entrance
41 Camp bakery, depot and garages, SS Clothing Works
42 Depot of the SS Clothing Works
43 Workshops of the German Equipment Works (DAW)

44 Concentration camp headquarters
45 Political department (Gestapo)
46 Barracks of the camp guard units
48 SS barracks and administration
49 SS site administration
50 Air-raid shelter ("Hollerith bunker")
53 SS officers mess ("Waldcasino")
54 Location of the death train at liberation
56 Main construction management of the Waffen-SS and police (construction depot)
57 Barracks of the SS combat troops
58 Garages
59 (SS) Porcelain factory Allach
60 SS technical weapons training institute
61 SS Clothing Works/tailors
62 "Dutch shed" (warehouse and workshops)

65 SS officers school for administrative duties
66 Reichsführer SS, dept. "F" (Dr. Fahrenkamp)
67 SS hospital
70 SS sports field
71 SS swimming facility
72 Entomology Institute
73 Plantation (herb garden), maintenance building
80 Präzifix workshops
81 Outside wall/fence of the concentration camp
82 Fence around the prisoners' camp, with guard towers
83 Crematorium area
84 Medicinal herb garden, the "Plantation"

The Dachau Concentration Camp, 1942-1945

After the failure of the Blitzkrieg ("lightning war") concept at the end of 1941, adapting the economy to the demands of a long, drawn-out war became a question of survival for the National Socialists. Massive numbers of concentration camp prisoners were forced to work in armaments production. The concentration camps were extended through a network of external work details and subcamps to a giant system of slave labor.

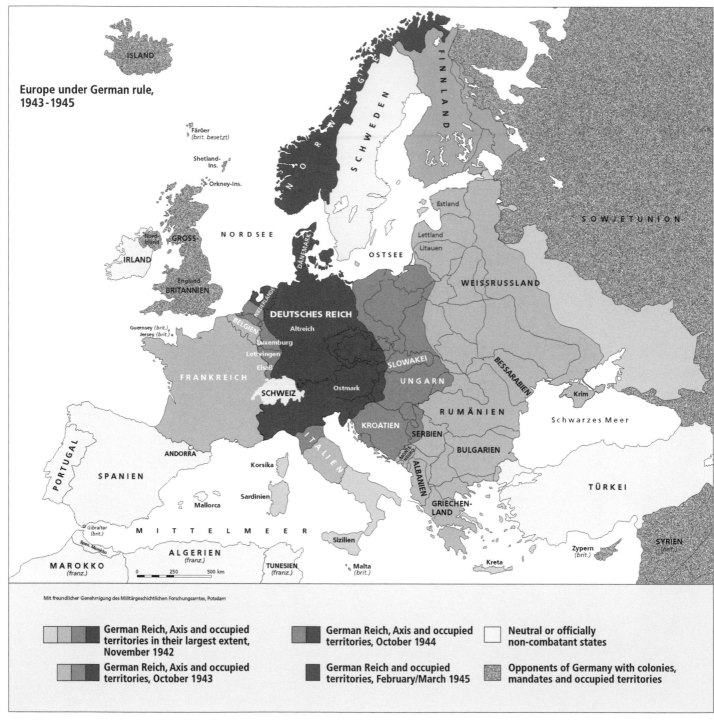

Europe under German rule, 1943-1945

ISLAND

Färöer (brit. besetzt)

Shetland-Ins.

Orkney-Ins.

NORWEGEN

SCHWEDEN

FINNLAND

SOWJETUNION

Estland

Lettland

Litauen

NORDSEE

Nord-Irland

GROSS-

IRLAND

England

BRITANNIEN

OSTSEE

DÄNEMARK

WEISSRUSSLAND

Guernsey (brit.)
Jersey (brit.)

NIEDERLANDE

BELGIEN

DEUTSCHES REICH

Altreich

Luxemburg

Lothringen

Elsaß

FRANKREICH

SCHWEIZ

Ostmark

SLOWAKEI

UNGARN

BESSARABIEN

Krim

RUMÄNIEN

Schwarzes Meer

KROATIEN

SERBIEN

BULGARIEN

MONTE NEGRO

ALBANIEN

GRIECHEN-LAND

TÜRKEI

PORTUGAL

SPANIEN

ANDORRA

Korsika

Sardinien

Mallorca

ITALIEN

Gibraltar (brit.)

Span. Marokko

MITTELMEER

Sizilien

Kreta

Zypern (brit.)

SYRIEN (brit.)

ALGERIEN (franz.)

TUNESIEN (franz.)

Malta (brit.)

MAROKKO (franz.)

0 250 500 km

Mit freundlicher Genehmigung des Militärgeschichtlichen Forschungsamtes, Potsdam

German Reich, Axis and occupied territories in their largest extent, November 1942	German Reich, Axis and occupied territories, October 1944
German Reich, Axis and occupied territories, October 1943	German Reich and occupied territories, February/March 1945
	Neutral or officially non-combatant states
	Opponents of Germany with colonies, mandates and occupied territories

The defeat of German troops at the gates of Moscow and the entry of the United States into the war signaled the failure of the Blitzkrieg concept. Adapting the economy to the demands of a long, drawn-out war became a question of survival for the National Socialists. At the end of February 1942, Hitler ordered that concentration camp prisoners be put to work in armaments production.

Converting the concentration camps into labor camps for slaves

On March 3, 1942, Himmler placed the Main Office of SS Economic Administration (WVHA) in charge of the concentration camps. Oswald Pohl, the head of this office, issued an order on April 30, 1942 that included the following points:

4. The camp commandant is fully responsible for the deployment of labor. This deployment must be exhaustive in the true sense of the word, in order to achieve maximum output...

5. There are no restrictions on the hours of work...

6. All circumstances that shorten work time (meals, roll call, etc.) are therefore to be reduced to the absolute minimum. Time consuming marches and lunch breaks solely for the purpose of eating are forbidden...

IMT Doc. 129-R

Extermination through work

Delivery of unsocial elements from the penal system to the Reichsführer SS for extermination through work.

All of the following are to be handed over: preventive detainees, Jews, Gypsies, Russians and Ukrainians, Poles serving over 3 years, Czechs or Germans serving over 8 years to be decided by the Reich Minister of Justice...

Notes taken during a meeting between the Reich Minister of Justice Otto Thierack and Heinrich Himmler, September 18 1942

IMT XXVI, Doc. 654 PS, 200-203

Crematorium ovens in the Buchenwald concentration camp

Due to the high death rate, the crematoriums had to be modernized and expanded in Buchenwald and other concentration camps in 1942.

Photo: SS 1943, MRD Besancon

Catastrophic death rate

The murderous work turned the prisoners into physical wrecks and the death rate reached enormous proportions. This hindered the mass deployment of prisoners in the armaments industry that had been planned for 1942.

Death rate in the concentration camps in the second half of 1942, based on a list from Oswald Pohl, the head of the SS WVHA

Month	Average	Deaths	Per cent
July	98,000	8,329	8.50
August	115,000	12,217	10.62
September	110,000	11,206	10.19
October	85,800	8,856	10.32
November	83,500	8,095	9.69
December	88,000	8,800	10.00

IMT Dok. PS-1469

Slave hunt

Himmler set quotas for the police on how many able-bodied prisoners were to be sent to the concentration camps and ordered that raids be carried out. Later, as German troops retreated before the advancing Red Army, any persons capable of working were taken from the local population ("evacuated") and deported directly to the concentration camps.

> To achieve the highest possible results during these raids, cinemas and churches were simply surrounded and then all the visitors ... were indiscriminately arrested and sent to the concentration camps.
>
> Report from Ernst Boepple, undersecretary in the General Government, during a visit to the Reich Chancellery, February 26, 1943. BA Berlin

> It is necessary that during the evacuation of these areas of the Ukraine, no person, no livestock, not a hundredweight of grain, not a track of railroad be left behind...
>
> Letter from Himmler to Hans-Adolf Prützmann, the Higher SS and Police Leader in the Ukraine, September 7, 1943. Reichsführer!, Heiber (ed.)

"Arrival", drawing by Vlastimir Kopač (1944-1945 in the Dachau concentration camp)
Muzej novejše zgodovine Slovenije, Ljubljana

> At the train station there were already a number of corpses thrown onto a waiting truck. But on leaving the station, still more prisoners died and so a few prisoners ... dragged along their dead comrades – their heads twisted backwards and their glassy eyes instilling fear in all who caught a glimpse of this procession of the dead. "I stood on the corner," Frau Weber [a civilian worker on the plantation] told me, "and cried in fright and a group of women also cried. They threw their hands in the air and exclaimed: God forbid that revenge be taken on us like this."
>
> Journal entry by Karel Kašák (1939-1945 in the Dachau concentration camp) about the arrival of a transport with 1,500 prisoners from the Ukraine at the train station in the city of Dachau, September 14, 1944. The notes of Karel Kašák.

Measures to maintain and exploit prisoner labor

In order to reduce the death rate among the prisoners, the SS leadership introduced a few "privileges". The prisoners were permitted to receive food packages. Doctors from the prisoner ranks were allowed to work as orderlies in the infirmary. The death rate began to fall in 1943.

Premiums

Prisoners who distinguish themselves through hard work, prudence, good conduct and exceptional productivity will now be rewarded with privileges.

They will be dispensed in the form of:
1. easing of imprisonment conditions,
2. extra provisions,
3. money premiums,
4. purchase of tobacco,
5. visit to the brothel.

Regulation from Oswald Pohl, head of the SS WVHA, on the dispensing of privileges to prisoners, May 15, 1943. IMT NO-400

Increasing number of prisoners in the concentration camps after 1942:

December	1942	88,000
August	1943	224,000
August	1944	534,000
January	1945	etwa 741,000 to 750,000

Gradual reduction in the death rate in the concentration camps during the first half of 1943

Month	Average	Deaths	Per cent
January	123,000	9,839	8
February	143,100	11,650	8.14
March	154,200	12,112	7.85
April	171,000	8,358	4.71
May	203,000	5,700	2.80
June	199,500	5,650	2.83

Based on a list from Oswald Pohl, head of the SS WVHA (excerpt) StA Nuremberg

Even in May 1943, when the death rate was at its lowest, the average life expectancy of a prisoner in a camp was less than three years. These figures do not include the victims of the mass killings in the extermination camps, nor of the atrocities committed by the death squads ("Einsatzgruppen").

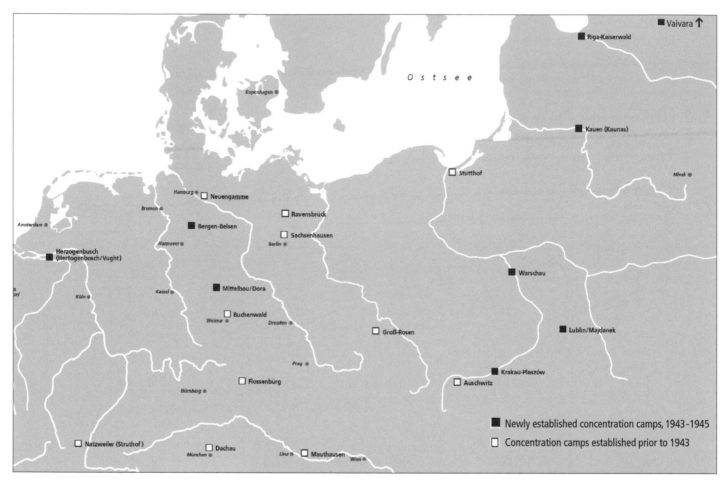

Map legend:

- ■ Newly established concentration camps, 1943-1945
- ☐ Concentration camps established prior to 1943

Camps marked on map: Vaivara, Riga-Kaiserwald, Kauen (Kaunas), Minsk, Stutthof, Neuengamme, Hamburg, Bremen, Ravensbrück, Bergen-Belsen, Sachsenhausen, Berlin, Amsterdam, Hannover, Warschau, Herzogenbusch (Hertogenbosch/Vught), Köln, Kassel, Mittelbau/Dora, Buchenwald, Weimar, Dresden, Groß-Rosen, Lublin/Majdanek, Prag, Krakau-Plaszów, Flossenbürg, Nürnberg, Auschwitz, Natzweiler (Struthof), Dachau, München, Linz, Mauthausen, Wien, Kopenhagen, Ostsee

In 1944, at the pinnacle of the "total war", a number of concentration camps were modified to serve new functions.

Lublin-Majdnek concentration camp
Beginning in 1942, the Lublin-Majdanek concentration camp was used by the SS as an extermination camp. From 1943 it served as an "invalid camp". This meant that prisoners unfit for work were concentrated here and simply left to die of starvation, or exposure to the freezing weather and catastrophic hygiene conditions.
Photo: after liberation 1944, Muzeum Majdanek

Herzogenbusch concentration camp (s´Hertogenbosch/Vught), established in January 1943
USHMM

Kauen concentration camp (Kaunas/Lithuania) In June 1943 the ghetto in Kauen was converted into a concentration camp. USHMM

Mittelbau-Dora concentration camp Initially set up in August 1943 as a subcamp of Buchenwald, by October 1944 it was an independent concentration camp. V-2 rockets were manufactured in large underground chambers. KZ-Gst. Mittelbau-Dora

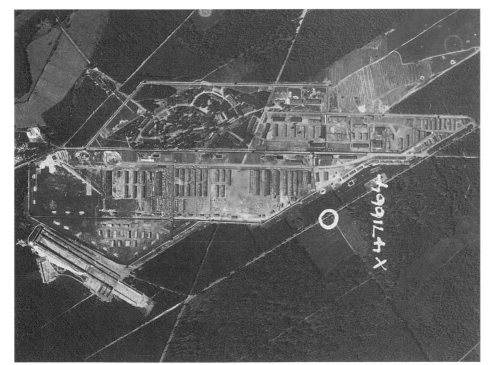

Bergen-Belsen concentration camp From 1943 the camp was used for so-called exchange Jews, who were to be offered to the Allies in exchange for German prisoners, money and goods. As of spring 1944 it served as an "invalid camp". Air Photo Library, University of Keele

Oswald Pohl The head of the Main Office of SS Economic Administration (WVHA), Pohl was placed in charge of the concentration camps in March 1942. After the war he was sentenced to death and executed in 1951. BA Koblenz

Murder and terror reached a peak in the Dachau concentration camp in 1941-1942. Starvation and disease, in particular a typhus epidemic in the winter of 1942-43, exacerbated the situation further. The measures ordered by the SS to reduce the death rate only began to have an impact in 1943. The prisoners were now allowed to receive packages of food and clothing. Work incentives were also introduced. The chances of survival improved, however, only for those able to work. The SS left the "invalids" simply to die in the camp or had them deported to the extermination camps. The increasing overcrowding of the camp in the course of 1944 caused the living conditions to drastically deteriorate. The number of prisoners in the entire Dachau camp system rose from around 10,000 at the end of 1942 to more than 63,000 by the end of 1944. The prisoners worked primarily in the subcamps. The main camp increasingly evolved into a camp for the sick.

View inside a barrack after liberation Photo: Lee Miller, April 30, 1945, Lee Miller Archives, Chiddingly

We are permitted to receive packages with food as well as tobacco and underwear. Food and tobacco can be placed in one package, but the underwear has to be sent in a separate package. The package has to be marked with "underwear" or "food", respectively.

This notice had to be included in every letter sent by a prisoner to his relatives at the end of 1942/beginning of 1943. KZ-Gst. Dachau

Camp brothel ("special building")
Yesterday, on April 16 [1944], on the main camp road six women were led to the back of the love barrack, the last, the 29th block. The whole camp walked in front of the barracks and regarded the women with great interest... The Dachau camp, or more exactly its prisoners, with only a few exceptions, ignored the love barracks. This quiet sabotage annoyed the men in the gatehouse so much that the duty leader summoned the barrack elders and threatened, warned and tried to persuade them.
The notes of Karel Kašák.

Prisoners working in the lumber yard,
marching between them a SS column, summer 1944
KZ-Gst. Dachau

Prisoners producing bullet casings KZ-Gst. Dachau

Nikifor Molokov, Soviet prisoner. Drawing by
Vlastimir Kopač, April 2, 1944.
Muzej novejše zgodovine Slovenije, Ljubljana

The "camp road" haircut
To be able to utilize human hair for the production of felt, an order was issued in August 1942
that the prisoners' hair was to be cut first upon
reaching a length of 2 cm. To make sure that
they were nevertheless recognizable as prisoners,
a 5 cm wide strip was shorn down the middle,
known as the "camp road". This measure was
later "solely" used to humiliate Soviet and Italian
prisoners.

Präzifix armaments workshop
One of our directors, named Sölter, now wants
one man to work two machines. He was told
that this wouldn't work. He replied: "then I will
just write a few reports. After a few of you get
whipped, the others will work."
Kupfer-Koberwitz, Dachauer Tagebücher

The bunker (camp prison) USHMM

Prisoners in marked civilian clothing
The civilian clothing of Jews murdered in the
extermination camps was marked with paint
and distributed to the prisoners.
Photo: Raphael Algoet, April 29, 1945, CEDGSC

Standing cell in the bunker
I was unable to lie down and I couldn't crouch,
it was best to just stand up, standing for six
days and six nights...A small 2.8 meter-high
chamber, in the ceiling a small window, and
that was it. Your elbows touch both sides of the
walls, your back is up against the wall behind
you and your knees pressed against the wall
in front of you. A little door let inside, bolted
from the outside with four iron bars. It is
not punishment or detention, that is torture,
straightforward medieval torture.
The notes of KarelKašák.

147

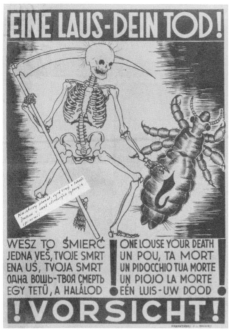

Poster "One Louse – Your Death",
December 1942 KZ-Gst. Dachau

Large crematorium ("barrack X") after liberation NA Washington

Returning from delousing
Drawing by Vlastimir Kopač, March 1945
Muzej noveje zgodovine Slovenije, Ljubljana

Ovens in the large crematorium NA Washington

The so-called "prisoner self-administration" enabled the SS to enforce its rule of terror by using prisoners designated to special functions (the camp, barrack and room elders, the capos and the infirmary personnel). In contrast to many other camps, in Dachau most of these special functions were in the hands of political prisoners. Many of them used their position to protect their fellow prisoners.

"Non-commissioned officer corps"

These roughly 40,000 German political and professional criminals … are my NCOs for the whole corporation. We have deployed so-called capos here. Consequently, one prisoner is the responsible overseer of 30, 40, 100 others. The moment he is a capo, he no longer sleeps where they do. He is responsible for ensuring that the productivity goals are achieved, that no sabotage occurs, that they are clean, that the beds are well made… He must therefore drive his men on. As soon as we are dissatisfied with him, he ceases to be a capo, and again sleeps with the rest of his men. He knows that they will then beat him to death on the first night…

Heinrich Himmler, speech to Wehrmacht generals, June 21, 1944. Himmler, Geheimreden

Advantages of self-administration

The system of prisoner self-administration was created as an extended arm of the SS to spread their terror into the furthest reaches of the camp, but as the camp grew larger, making it impossible for the camp leadership to oversee this administration, it provided more and more opportunities to act against the SS terror and extermination system. Langbein, …nicht wie Schafe.

Karl Frey (b. 1900) was imprisoned as early as 1933 in the Dachau concentration camp because of his political opposition. As room elder in the penal block and then later as barrack elder, first in barrack 26 (clergy block) and then in barrack 22, he was held in high regard by his fellow prisoners. His efforts to protect the prisoners included refusing to carry out SS orders to beat them on the trestle. Photo: 1945, private ownership

Adolf (Adi) Maislinger (1903-1985)
The German Communist Adolf (Adi) Maislinger was sent to the Dachau concentration camp in 1942 after serving an eight-year prison sentence for resistance activities. Here he was made capo of the disinfection detail. As the SS avoided the disinfection area for fear of infection, he was able to hide and protect prisoners there. A radio was hidden there as well, enabling the prisoners to keep themselves informed about the course of the war.

The photo shows Adolf Maislinger during a tour of the Dachau Concentration Camp Memorial Site, around 1980. KZ-Gst. Dachau

First imprisoned in 1933, **Karl Kapp** (1898-1965) was sent to the Dachau concentration camp in January 1936 for a second time. As head capo of the garage construction detail in 1940 he was infamous for his acts of brutality. Between 1941 and 1942 camp elder, he was the most hated and feared prisoner functionary, particularly among the foreign prisoners. He subjected them to brutal beatings and harassed them with exercise drills and punishment reports.

Karl Kapp (front right), 1936.
"Illustrierter Beobachter"

Christof Knoll was in the Dachau concentration camp from September 1933 to August 1942 and again from March 1943 until liberation. As head capo on the "plantation" and then as block elder in the penal block, he became notorious for his brutality. At the postwar Dachau trials he was sentenced to death and executed in May 1946.

Christof Knoll as defendant in the first Dachau Concentration Camp Trial, December 7, 1945.
NA Washington

Knoll conditioning
Knoll suddenly shouted: Move it! Punishment drill in the yard! And the person on room duty started hitting us with a club, and we had to run fast … and so ran outside barefoot and were soon covered with mud. And then we came back and naturally made everything dirty… Lick it off! So we licked the dirt with our tongues. And they beat us, and some of us were killed in the process. That was the Knoll conditioning. Kulka, in: Pingel, Häftlinge

After the war began, the concentration camp personnel was integrated into the Waffen-SS. As the network of subcamps expanded, the SS required more guard soldiers. "Ethnic Germans" from southeastern Europe and regular Wehrmacht soldiers were recruited. The place of deployment changed constantly. Concentration camp guards were sent to the front, while members of the Waffen-SS no longer able to actively serve on the front were assigned to duty in the concentration camps.

Martin Weiss had already served as technical supervisor of the Dachau concentration camp in 1933. From 1938 he served as adjutant to the camp commandants Loritz and Piorkowski. He was appointed commandant of the Neuengamme concentration camp in April 1940. In September 1942 he was transferred to Dachau to serve as commandant. In 1943 he was placed in charge of the Lublin-Majdanek concentration camp. In May 1944 he was then appointed department head of the Office Group D in the SS Main Office of Economic Administration and in the same year ordered to supervise the sub-camp complex at Mühldorf. After the war an American military court sentenced him to death. He was executed in 1946.

Martin Weiss (1905–1946), commandant of the Dachau concentration camp 1942–1943

Photo: SS Files, BA Berlin

Eduard Weiter (1889–1945), commandant of the Dachau concentration camp 1943–1945.

Eduard Weiter in the uniform of the Bavarian State Police, 1920s.

Order issued by the Reichsführer SS to the head of the SS Main Office on the transfer of 10,000 Wehrmacht soldiers to the Waffen-SS, May 11, 1944. BA Berlin

Eduard Weiter was administrative head of several SS regiments before he became commandant of the Dachau concentration camp in November 1943. He showed little interest in improving the increasingly dramatic situation facing the prisoners towards the end of the war. He gave his protective custody camp leaders free reign and retreated into administrative work. Weiter shot himself on May 6, 1945 at Itter Castle, a subcamp of Dachau. BayHStA

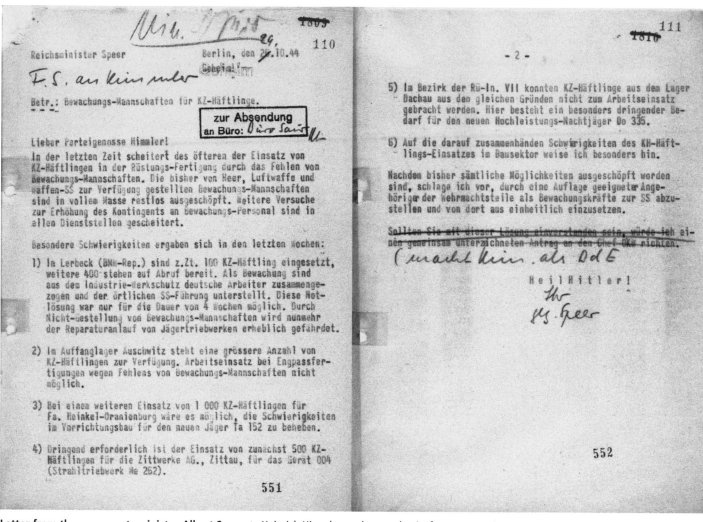

Reichsminister Speer   Berlin, den 29.10.44
                            Geheim!

Betr.: Bewachungs-Mannschaften für KZ-Häftlinge.

Lieber Parteigenosse Himmler!

In der letzten Zeit scheitert des öfteren der Einsatz von
KZ-Häftlingen in der Rüstungs-Fertigung durch das Fehlen von
Bewachungs-Mannschaften. Die bisher von Heer, Luftwaffe und
Waffen-SS zur Verfügung gestellten Bewachungs-Mannschaften
sind in vollem Masse restlos ausgeschöpft. Weitere Versuche
zur Erhöhung des Kontingents an Bewachungs-Personal sind in
allen Dienststellen gescheitert.

Besondere Schwierigkeiten ergaben sich in den letzten Wochen:

1) In Lerbeck (BMW-Rep.) sind z.Zt. 100 KZ-Häftling eingesetzt,
   weitere 400 stehen auf Abruf bereit. Als Bewachung sind
   aus dem Industrie-Werkschutz deutsche Arbeiter zusammengezogen und der örtlichen SS-Führung unterstellt. Diese Not-
   lösung war nur für die Dauer von 4 Wochen möglich. Durch
   Nicht-Gestellung von Bewachungs-Mannschaften wird nunmehr
   der Reparaturanlauf von Jägertriebwerken erheblich gefährdet.

2) Im Auffanglager Auschwitz steht eine grössere Anzahl von
   KZ-Häftlingen zur Verfügung. Arbeitseinsatz bei Engpassfer-
   tigungen wegen Fehlens von Bewachungs-Mannschaften nicht
   möglich.

3) Bei einem weiteren Einsatz von 1 000 KZ-Häftlingen für
   Fa. Heinkel-Oranienburg wäre es möglich, die Schwierigkeiten
   im Vorrichtungsbau für den neuen Jäger Ta 152 zu beheben.

4) Dringend erforderlich ist der Einsatz von zunächst 500 KZ-
   Häftlingen für die Zittwerke AG., Zittau, für das Gerät 004
   (Strahltriebwerk Me 262).

551

- 2 -

5) Im Bezirk der Rü-In. VII konnten KZ-Häftlinge aus dem Lager
   Dachau aus den gleichen Gründen nicht zum Arbeitseinsatz
   gebracht werden. Hier besteht ein besonders dringender Be-
   darf für den neuen Hochleistungs-Nachtjäger Do 335.

6) Auf die darauf zusammenhängen Schwierigkeiten des KZ-Häft-
   lings-Einsatzes im Bausektor weise ich besonders hin.

Nachdem bisher sämtliche Möglichkeiten ausgeschöpft worden
sind, schlage ich vor, durch eine Auflage geeignete Angehörige der Wehrmachtsteile als Bewachungskräfte zur SS abzu-
stellen und von dort aus einheitlich einzusetzen.

Sollten Sie mit dieser Lösung einverstanden sein, würde ich einen gemeinsam unterzichneten Antrag an den Chef OKW richten.

Heil Hitler!

gez. Speer

552

Letter from the armaments minister, Albert Speer, to Heinrich Himmler on the guard units for concentration camp prisoners, October 29, 1944. BA Berlin

In 1941 a camp ("SS penal camp") was set up within the bunker, primarily for SS men sentenced by SS and police courts to prison terms or death. The executions took place at the SS shooting range near Hebertshausen. In 1943 a branch of the SS penal camp was set up in the Allach subcamp. The SS prisoners, numbering around 1,000, were forced to work for BMW.

Hans Hespe was a member of the Police Battalion 105 that was involved in mass executions in eastern Europe. For absence without leave, he was sentenced to five years prison in September 1942. He was sent to the SS penal camps at Dachau and Allach. In February 1945 he was drafted into the SS Dirlewanger unit and fell into Soviet captivity.

Hans Hespe (1907-1968) as member of the Police Battalion 105 (Bremen).
Photo: private ownership

SS judges inspect the penal company of the SS penal camp in the bunker courtyard, around 1941-42 Photo: SS, BA Ludwigsburg

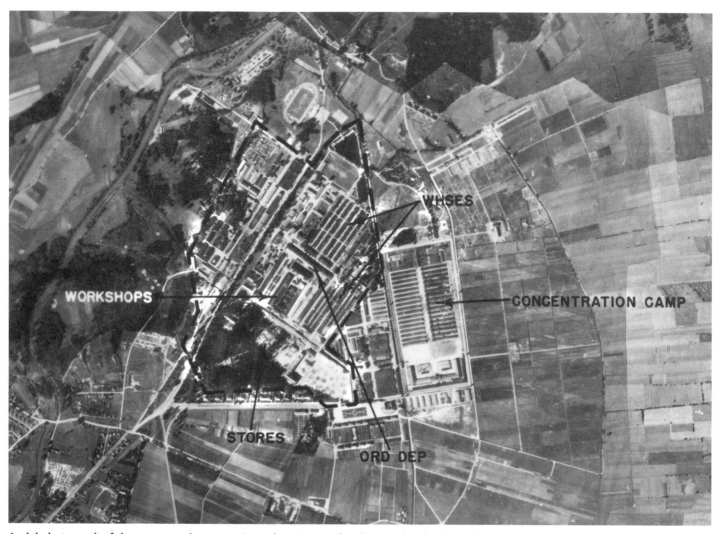

Aerial photograph of the concentration camp, September 13, 1944 This photograph, taken by an Allied reconnaissance plane, contains information for aerial bombardment. Buildings in the SS camp were bombed on numerous occasions, but the prisoner camp was always marked as a protected area. Lbdb Carls

New Prisoner Groups

Until 1942, Poles, Germans and Czechs comprised the largest prisoner groups in the Dachau concentration camp. As of summer 1942, they were joined by Soviet prisoners. Soon after, Yugoslavs were sent, and beginning in 1943, French, Dutch, Belgian and Italian prisoners were committed. After the Allies landed in Normandy in summer 1944, the Gestapo evacuated the camps in France, Belgium and the Netherlands and transferred the prisoners to concentration camps in the Reich, including Dachau. In summer 1944, the Nazi regime deported Hungarian and Lithuanian Jews to the subcamps near Kaufering and Mühldorf, while residents of Warsaw and German regime opponents were sent to the main Dachau camp. Children were among the deported as well. Beginning in summer 1944, women were also sent to the subcamps. The conditions under which the respective prisoner groups lived were determined by their place in the SS prisoner hierarchy. At the "top" were German prisoners, at the "bottom" Jewish, Soviet and Italian prisoners. Their chances of survival steadily worsened.

Transport of 2,145 prisoners from the Compiègne camp
to the Dachau concentration camp, June 18, 1944
FNDIRP

In 1941-1942, over 4,000 Soviet prisoners of war were sent to the Dachau concentration camp for execution; they were never officially registered. Soviet citizens deported to the Dachau concentration came directly from the occupied territories, where the German army and SS troops depopulated the entire region in an effort to destroy the partisan movement at its roots. Prisoners of war and forced laborers already in the Reich were also sent to the concentration camps, due to "refusing to work" or "attempting to escape". Soviet prisoners belonged to the lowest level of the prisoner hierarchy in the camp. Alongside Jewish prisoners, they had the least chance of survival. They were also least willing to submit to the camp regime and undertook the most escape attempts. Well over a hundred Soviet prisoners were murdered directly in the camp. Between 1942 and 1945 a total of at least 25,000 Soviet citizens were imprisoned in Dachau. After returning to the Soviet Union many of them were subjected to persecution for alleged collaboration.

The Soviet prisoner Lonja, drawing by Vlastimir Kopač (1944-1945 in the Dachau concentration camp), March 26, 1945.
The portrait clearly shows the "camp road" haircut that was temporarily used to make the prisoners recognizable as inmates.
Muzej novejše zgodovine Slovenije, Ljubljana

Timofei Farenjuk, "shot while trying to escape", because he ran towards the gate of the plantation. KZ-Gst. Dachau

Timofei Farenjuk was arrested in the Soviet Union and deported to Dachau, where he arrived in July 1942. On March 16, 1943, he was shot by the SS during an "attempted escape".

Ivan Savinych

There are exactly 19 of them, boys aged between 10 and 14, two are almost 15. Almost all of them have been living in various German concentration camps for two years now…
Not one of the boys has a clue where his mother and father are. Almost all of them answer that their father is at the front and the mother at some unknown location. Only God knows how and when these children, deadened by camp life and robbed of every childhood joy, will be reunited with their parents, if at all.
I took one of them aside and sketched him in full figure on a piece of cardboard I had with me. He is the 11-year-old Ivan Savinych…
He comes from Charkov and has the prisoner number 58632.

Secret journal entry by Karel Kašák on a plantation work detail with Russian children, March 1945 (excerpt) Notes by Karel Kašák.

The 11-year-old Ivan Savinych on the plantation, drawing by Karel Kašák, March 23, 1945. Památník Terezín

German troops invaded Yugoslavia in 1941. From summer 1942, some 7,700 Slovenes, Croatians, Serbs and members of other ethnic groups in the country were sent to the Dachau concentration camp and its subcamps. Slovenian prisoners formed the largest group. The German occupiers and their local helpers arrested, deported and murdered Jews and Roma as well as persons suspected of being Communist partisans. In addition, members of monarchist and fascist groups were also persecuted if they refused to cooperate with the Germans. The Communists were able to establish their own organizational structures in the camp.

Vlastimir Kopač (b. 1913)
The Slovenian Vlastimir Kopač was arrested in October 1943 for working illegally as a graphic artist for the Slovenian Communist Party.
He arrived in the Dachau concentration camp on January 8, 1944, and was assigned to the bookbinding workshop, where he had opportunities to draw in secret.
After liberation he returned to Lubljana where he was convicted in one of the notorious, ideologically tainted "Dachau trials" of having been a "Gestapo agent". After clearing his name, he was active in various associations for concentration camp victims. KZ-Gst. Dachau

Ivan Trinajstič (b. 1919) The Croat Ivan Trinajstič was sent to a POW camp in Sangershausen as a soldier in the Royal Yugoslav Army in 1941. During the repatriation of Croat prisoners of war he fell into the hands of Tito partisans in May 1942, who in turn handed him over to the Italians. They held him captive until the capitulation of Italy in September 1943. Shortly after being set free he was arrested by the Germans. He arrived in the Dachau concentration camp in October 1943. Here he was assigned to the work detail that had to bring the corpses to the crematorium. In April 1944 he was moved to the Gendorf subcamp and in March 1945 to the Mühldorf-Mettenheim subcamp. After liberation the secret police in Yugoslavia suspected him of having been a "spy for the Germans". Photo: 2001, private ownership

Gavrilo (Djordje) Dočić (1881-1950)
Gavrilo Dočić was elected Serbian orthodox Patriarch in 1938. As a Serb nationalist and monarchist, he maintained close ties with the Serbian fascists. However, because he spoke out publicly against a treaty with Germany and its Axis partners, he was interned after the German invasion in 1941.

He spent a few weeks in the Dachau concentration camp in September 1944. He returned to Belgrade in 1946 and resumed his official duties. Photo: (presumably from the late 1940s) Mladenović, Memoari

To suppress resistance in the occupied territories, Hitler issued the "Night and Fog" decree on December 7, 1941, which ordered the death penalty as the general punishment for resistance activities. To increase intimidation, relatives were not to be informed about the fate of the victim. Prisoners who were not immediately executed were deported to Reich territory, where they were usually incarcerated in a concentration camp. Beginning in summer 1944, over 2,200 "night and fog" prisoners were sent to the Dachau concentration camp. They were housed in special barracks, were not allowed to receive mail, and were not sent to subcamps.

"state of uncertainty about the fate"

It is the long standing will of the Führer that in the case of attacks against the Reich or the occupying forces in the occupied territories, the culprits shall be subjected to different measures than those used so far. The Führer is of the opinion that for such acts prison sentences, even life sentences, would be considered a sign of weakness. An effective and lasting deterrent can only be achieved with the death penalty or measures that keep the relatives and the rest of the population in a state of uncertainty about the fate of the culprits. Transfer to Germany serves this purpose…

Directive issued by Wilhelm Keitel, Supreme Commander in the High Command of the Wehrmacht ("Night and Fog" decree), December 12, 1941 (excerpt) StA Nuremberg

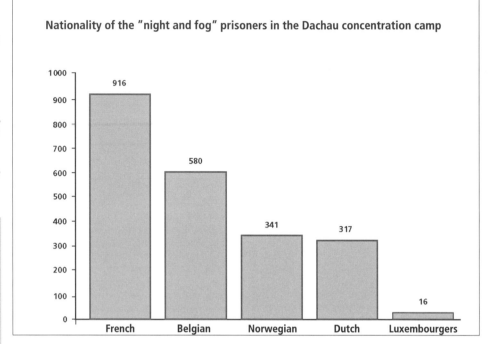

Nationality of the "night and fog" prisoners in the Dachau concentration camp

(Bar chart values: French 916, Belgian 580, Norwegian 341, Dutch 317, Luxembourgers 16)

Nico Rost (1896-1967) The Dutch writer and Communist Nico Rost moved to Berlin in the 1920s where he became acquainted with leftist writers. In 1933 he was imprisoned for a short time in the Oranienburg concentration camp and then extradited. He moved to Brussels where he translated works of German authors into Dutch. After the Netherlands and Belgium were occupied, Rost joined the resistance movement and was arrested at the beginning of 1943. He arrived in the Dachau concentration camp via the Vught camp (Herzogenbusch concentration camp) in June 1944 as a "night and fog" prisoner. He kept secret notes daily right up till liberation. He published his journal in 1946 under the title "Goethe in Dachau". In 1955, after visiting the camp grounds, he wrote the booklet "I was in Dachau again". Nico Rost was a key figure in establishing the Dachau Concentration Camp Memorial Site.

Photo: 1930s, Collectie Letterkundig Museum, The Hague

In the Dachau concentration camp and its subcamps there were over 1,800 Belgians, 2,100 Dutch and 467 Luxembourgers, including several hundred women. They were mostly victims of the mass arrests launched in 1943 that were supposed to break the ever-increasing resistance against the German occupation. The deportations to German concentration camps reached a climax in summer 1944, after the Allies had landed in Normandy. The Gestapo also charged large numbers of forced laborers with allegedly refusing to work and sentenced them to imprisonment in concentration camps.

Eugène Ost (1913-2001) The student Eugène Ost was expelled from university in Luxembourg for refusing to join the ethnic German movement. As a prospective teacher he refused again in April 1942. Transferred to Germany as punishment, he was eventually arrested in June 1942 when he refused to swear an oath to Hitler. The Gestapo committed him to the Dachau concentration camp in August 1942. Working as a clerk in the malaria experiment station, Ost was able to preserve important documents about these experiments. After liberation he made them available to the prosecution in the Dachau trials. Ost wrote numerous articles about the Dachau concentration camp and was active in the leadership of the Luxembourg Prisoner Association and the International Dachau Committee for many years.

Photo: 1946, private ownership

Arthur Haulot (1913-2005) Arthur Haulot had maintained contact with the Belgian Socialist leadership that had immigrated to Great Britain. He was arrested in September 1941 and taken to the Mauthausen concentration camp as a "night and fog" prisoner. In November 1942, close to death, he was transferred to the Dachau camp. After recuperating, he worked as an orderly in the infirmary, where he also secretly kept notes. As a trusted intermediary for the Belgian prisoners he was one of the founding members of the International Camp Committee in spring 1945. After liberation he wrote a report on the Dachau concentration camp and composed poems about his memories of the camp. He was honored for his literary work with many awards. Haulot represented the Belgian camp survivors in the International Dachau Committee and served as its vice-president for many years.

Arthur Haulot as head orderly of the typhus block, 1944 Photo: illegally taken by Jean Brichaux, KZ-Gst. Dachau

Johan E. A. Post Uiterweer (b. 1917) Johan E. A. Post Uiterweer was a member of a Dutch resistance group. Arrested in February 1941, he was sent to the Sachsenhausen concentration camp. He was one of the first Dutch prisoners to be sent to the Dachau camp in October 1942, where he was assigned to the laundry detail. He survived the medical experiments that were performed on him, but suffered from their effects for his entire life. He was liberated in the Dachau camp in 1945.

Dutch prisoners standing in front the Jourhaus, far right Post Uiterweer

Photo: shortly after liberation 1945, KZ-Gst. Dachau

French resistance against the German occupation became a mass movement in 1943. The German occupation authorities fought resistance activities by making arrests, taking hostages and carrying out executions. Increasing numbers of prisoners were sent to concentration camps, in particular to Natzweiler (Vosges), Buchenwald, Neuengamme and Dachau. After the Allies landed in Normandy in summer 1944, the SS deported tens of thousands of French citizens to concentration camps on Reich territory. Altogether about 100,000 French citizens were deported to German concentration camps, about 15,000 to the Dachau camp.

Edmond Michelet (1889-1970)
Edmond Michelet, a leading member of a Catholic youth organization in the 1920s, joined the emerging resistance movement as early as 1940 and founded the group "Mouvement Liberté". As regional leader of the "Mouvements unis de la Résistance", he was arrested by the Gestapo in February 1943 and sent to the Dachau concentration camp in September 1943. Assigned to the disinfectory work detail, he was able to move around the camp freely and make numerous contacts. He was also able to exert considerable influence in the infirmary. As a trusted intermediary of the French prisoners he was a member of the International Camp Committee in 1945. After liberation he returned home, where he became one of France's leading politicians and served in various ministerial posts. KZ-Gst. Dachau

Charles Delestraint (1899-1945)
In 1940 Charles Delestraint was general of the tank corps and direct superior of Charles de Gaulle. One of the first resistance fighters, Delestraint was commissioned by de Gaulle, who from exile in London was calling for the French to resist, with building up a military resistance movement in 1942. In June 1943 he was arrested by the Gestapo. Despite torture he disclosed no information. He was then taken to the Natzweiler concentration camp as a "night and fog" prisoner. After this camp was evacuated, he was deported to the Dachau camp in September 1944, where his former position and function initially remained unknown to the SS. When they found out who he was in March 1945, he was taken to the bunker as a "special prisoner". Presumably on orders from Himmler, he was shot by SS men in the crematorium courtyard on April 19, 1945. A memorial plaque in the Panthéon in Paris commemorates his fate. Photo: 1938, Collection Dr. F. Y. Guillin

Germain Auboiroux (1896-1947)
Germain Auboiroux was active in the resistance as a trade unionist and functionary of the French Communist Party in the departement Corrèze. The Vichy government had him arrested and sentenced to five years forced labor. In October 1943 he was transferred from Eysses prison to the Compiègne camp and in June 1944 sent to the Dachau concentration camp. He assumed a leading position among the French Communist prisoners. He died in 1947 from the effects of his imprisonment.

Portrait by Georges Beauché, drawn during imprisonment in the Eysses prison, around 1943
KZ-Gst. Dachau

After Italy capitulated on September 8, 1943 and was occupied by Germany, over 9,500 Italians were deported to the Dachau concentration camp. Most of them were partisans, inmates of military prisons and prisoners of war who had engaged in resistance activities. As the Italians were regarded as renegade allies and "traitors", they were subjected to particularly brutal abuse and humiliation by the SS guard units. The death rate among the Italians was extremely high.

Giovanni Melodia (1915 - 2003)
Giovanni Melodia refused military service because of his pacifist-socialist convictions. Arrested as early as 1939, he was sentenced to a long prison term by an Italian military court. After the Italian capitulation, he was sent to the Dachau concentration camp on October 13, 1943. Shortly before liberation he made contact with the International Camp Committee. After returning home he became president of the Italian Survivors' Committee.
Photo: June 1945, private ownership

Enrico Piccaluga (b. 1925)
The student and partisan Enrico Piccaluga was arrested at the end of July 1944 and deported to the Dachau concentration camp in October. He worked in a bomb defusing and debris clearing detail in Munich and at the Mühldorf subcamp. After an escape attempt in January 1945 he was severely mistreated by the SS and detained in the bunker. He was then placed back in the main Dachau camp, where he remained imprisoned until the end of the war. Photo: November 1945, Private ownership

Riccardo Goruppi
Edoardo Goruppi
Riccardo Goruppi was arrested with his father Edoardo near Trieste in November 1944 for partisan activities. Sent to the Dachau concentration camp in December 1944, they were then subjected to extreme hard labor in its various subcamps. The father died under the merciless strain of these working conditions. After liberation, Riccardo Goruppi had to be treated for many months in a hospital before he could return to Trieste.

Riccardo Goruppi Photo: 1944, private ownership **Edoardo Goruppi** Photo: 1944, private ownership

After the assassination attempt on Hitler on July 20, 1944, the Gestapo launched a large-scale arrest operation in August 1944 under the codename "Operation Thunderstorm". Former functionaries and parliament members from the parties of the Weimar Republic were arrested, as were numerous political opponents who had already been imprisoned in concentration camps in the 1930s. The Nazi regime wanted to eliminate the possiblity of an uprising. Of the thousands arrested, 860 were sent to the Dachau concentration camp.

Franz Wirsching (1876-1945)
A member of the SPD, Franz Wirsching was secretary of the local committee of the General German Trade Union Association in Würzburg until 1933. He was taken into protective custody for two months in 1933. He was rearrested in 1942 for circulating anti-regime literature and sentenced to a 15-month prison term. In August 1944 the Gestapo arrested him again as part of "Operation Thunderstorm" and sent him to the Dachau camp, where he died in February 1945.
Photo: State Police Records, Würzburg office, 1942, StA Würzburg

Jean Stock (1893-1965)
The SPD councilor in Aschaffenburg and director of the Social Democratic newspaper "Aschaffenburger Volkszeitung" was temporarily taken into protective custody in March 1933 and August 1940. During "Operation Thunderstorm" he was arrested again in August 1944 and imprisoned in the Dachau concentration camp until early September. Photo: private ownership

Polish prisoners

After the mass deportations of 1940, under the pretense of "refusing to work," mainly Polish forced laborers were sent the Dachau concentration camp beginning in 1942. After the suppression of the Warsaw city uprising in the summer of 1944, the SS deported almost 70,000 civilians to concentration camps. Over 3,000 of these Poles were sent to the Dachau concentration camp.

Greek prisoners

Of the more than 1,000 Greek prisoners imprisoned in the Dachau camp, the majority were arrested on suspicion of involvement in the resistance movement. Beginning in mid-1944, many hundreds of Greek Jews were transferred from the Auschwitz concentration camp to the subcamps at Mühldorf and Kaufering.

Spanish prisoners

After the Spanish Civil War ended in 1939, hundreds of thousands of republic supporters fled from Franco's dictatorship to France. Most of them were put into internment camps. With the capitulation of France in 1940, the SS deported around 15,000 of them to concentration camps. Some 600 Spaniards were sent to the Dachau camp.

Tadeusz Biernacki (b. 1923)
Tadeusz Biernacki was arrested in June 1940 for being a member of a Polish boy scouts association. He was deported to Germany as a forced laborer. Caught in possession of a scout's cap in 1943, he was sent to the Dachau camp, where he was abused in a series of malaria experiments. Between 1943 and 1945 he was sent to different subcamps. After the war he became chairman of the Polish Prisoners Association. Photo: May 1945, private ownership

Nikos Zachariadis (1903-1973)
Appointed general secretary of the Greek Communist Party (KKE) in 1929, Nikos Zachariadis was arrested in 1936. In 1941, while still in prison, he began organizing the resistance against the Italian and German occupation. He was deported to the Dachau concentration camp at the end of 1941. On May 29, 1945, he returned to Greece and reassumed leadership of the KKE. After the Communists were defeated in the civil war in 1949, he went into exile in Moscow. He returned to Greece in 1956. Hellenic Educational Encyclopedia, 1991

SS transport of prisoners from the Eysses central prison in Villeneuve-sur-Lot, France, to the Dachau concentration camp, 30 May, 1944 Photo: FNDIRP

Beginning in 1941, SS death squads, German police and army units murdered thousands of Roma in the General Government, the occupied areas of the Soviet Union and in Serbia. In November 1941, 5,000 Roma from the Austrian Burgenland were deported to the Lodz ghetto. They died of typhus or were murdered in mobile gas vans. On orders from Himmler, from 1943 to 1944, the SS deported about 22,600 Sinti and Roma to the Auschwitz concentration camp, where more than 19,300 died. The last survivors were transported to concentration camps in the "Reich" in August 1944 to be used as force labor.

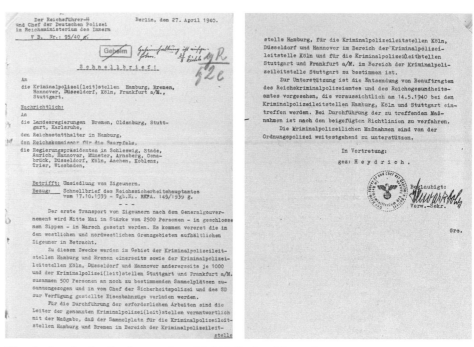

Himmler's order for the deportation of 2,500 Sinti and Roma from western Germany to occupied Poland, April 27, 1940 BayHStA

Transport of Sinti and Roma from Remscheid to the extermination camp Auschwitz,
March 1943 Police photo, Historisches Zentrum Remscheid

Concentration camp or forced sterilization
One day I was ordered to report to the Gestapo and was told that if I didn't want to go to a concentration camp, I would have to be sterilized. I had no other choice than to give in to this pressure, since even if I had preferred the camp, I would not have been spared there either. The sterilization was carried out by Dr. St. in Munich.

Report from the Sinto Peter H. about his persecution, in 1946 (excerpt) StadtA Munich

Like Peter H., many Sinti and Roma who were not deported were forcibly sterilized in 1943-1944.

The young Sinti girl Settela Steinbach during the deportation from the Dutch camp Westerbork to the extermination camp Auschwitz-Birkenau, May 15, 1944 Herinneringscentrum Kamp Westerbork

Settela Steinbach was murdered in a gas chamber along with her mother and siblings on the night of August 3, 1944.

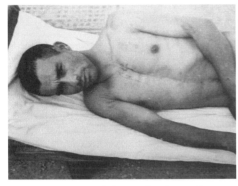

A Sinto as victim of the medical experiments in the Dachau concentration camp USHMM

Maximilian (Max) Rose (1899-1942)
Max Rose was arrested in Bayreuth in 1941 because of his Sinti ancestry. In early November 1942 he arrived with a transport from the Ravensbrück concentration camp at the Dachau camp. He died there two weeks later. DZ Sinti und Roma

As of 1941, the SS held a number of "special prisoners" captive in the bunker of the Dachau concentration camp. They included prominent German and foreign opponents of the regime. These prisoners received better provisions and were not required to work. In April 1945 they were taken to South Tyrol where they were liberated by Italian partisans and US troops on May 4, 1945.

Martin Niemöller (1892-1984)
The Protestant pastor Martin Niemöller gradually shifted from being a supporter of Hitler in the early 1930s to a decisive opponent of the Nazi dictatorship. As spokesman of the "Confessing Church" he was arrested in Berlin in 1937. After being held for a time in the Sachsenhausen concentration camp, he was transferred as a special prisoner to the bunker in the Dachau camp in July 1941. After the war, Martin Niemöller, as member of the "Council of Protestant Churches in Germany", played a key role in formulating the "Stuttgart confession of guilt" of 1945. He spoke out against rearming West Germany and called for an understanding with the Soviet bloc.

Martin Niemöller after liberation in Niederdorf, South Tyrol, May 1945
SV-Bilderdienst, Munich

Richard Stevens (1896-1968)
In 1939 Major Stevens was working for the British Special Intelligence Service (SIS) as head of the base in the Netherlands. On November 9, 1939, he and another intelligence officer were kidnapped by an SS commando unit in Venlo. They were taken for interrogation to Berlin and then to the Sachsenhausen concentration camp. In December 1941 Stevens was transferred to the Dachau camp and imprisoned in the bunker as a special prisoner. He was liberated in South Tyrol on May 4, 1945.

Photo: Richard Stevens after his arrest in November 1939, police records photo, published in the "Völkischer Beobachter", November 22, 1939.

Georg Elser (1903-1945)
On November 8, 1939, Georg Elser attempted to assassinate Hitler by detonating a bomb in the Bürgerbraukeller in Munich. Arrested shortly afterwards, he was sent to the Sachsenhausen concentration camp as a special prisoner. Elser was transferred to Dachau in February or March 1943. He was assigned to several different cells in the bunker presumably to await a show trial after the end of the war. He was kept in strict solitary confinement and placed under the constant guard of an SS man. On April 9, 1945, on orders from Himmler, Georg Elser was murdered by the SS at the crematorium.

Georg Elser after his arrest, 1939-40
Schweizerisches BA

Until the final phase of the war, there were only male prisoners in the Dachau concentration camp. Beginning in the summer of 1944, the SS deported about 7,000 mostly Jewish women to the subcamps of Dachau to perform forced labor. With the evacuation transports of early 1945, an increasing number of women were sent to the main camp. Women were subjected to the same harsh conditions of imprisonment as men. But women also had to bear the added degradations of sexual violence, of constant disrobing, of physical examination to determine their fitness for work, and of a lack of hygienic facilities.

Female prisoners listed according to nationality 1943-1945, based on entries in the admissions register

Hungary	5,211	Greece	12
Poland	1,542	Latvia	7
The Netherlands	198	Romania	6
Yugoslavia	189	San Salvador	3
Italy	95	Switzerland	3
German Reich	102	Bulgaria	2
Lithuania	226	Denmark	1
Belgium	38	Iraq	1
Czechoslovakia	33	Turkey	1
France	71	Stateless	3
Soviet Union	33		

This ghost is me

One day while I was on my way to one of the corners of the yard, prepared to even dig out worms if I couldn't find any grass, I passed by a window. I was suddenly startled... An old shriveled up lady stared out at me from her deep-set eyes – a bony phantom... I hastily looked around to see who this figure was, this head on a stalk that sent more fear through me than anything I had ever seen in my life. "That's me," I realized. "This ghost is me..."

Tuvel Bernstein, Die Näherin. Erinnerungen einer Überlebenden; Tuvel Bernstein was in the Dachau concentration camp, 1944-1945

Female prisoner in the Allach subcamp after liberation, 1945 FNDIRP

Sarah Benatar, Giovanna Hasson, Anna Coen

On July 20, 1944, the SS and Wehrmacht deported the entire Jewish population of Rhodes to the Auschwitz extermination camp. Sarah Benatar, Giovanna Hasson and Anna Coen were among the some 1,000 Greek women who were then transported from there to the Dachau camp in October 1944. They were forced to work as slave laborers in several subcamps of the Kaufering complex until liberation.

Impossible to keep up

In the summer of 1944 ... as I had to collect the women's personal possessions, I was confronted with a terrifying sight. Hollowed cheeks, pale figures ... shaved heads ... swaying between the trucks and the building materials site 700 meters away, each carrying a heavy cement sack on her back ... these women had to accomplish the same amount as the men. Each one had to load or unload 100 cement sacks per day ... given the poor hygiene and nourishment this work goal was impossible to achieve...

A prisoner's account of the work of women in the Mühldorf subcamp KZ-Gst. Dachau

---

Jewish women from Hungary with their babies after liberation
Many women were pregnant when they were deported in 1944. The SS forced them to abort. Only in the final months did they allow women to give birth to their children.

Photo: Sidney Blau, NA, Washington

				Frauen:		
119.920	27. Oktober 1944	Benatar	Sarah	Ital.-Jüdin	8. 7. 20.	Rodi
119.921	v. KL Auschwitz	Levi-Menasce	Ester	" "	2. 2. 13.	Milas
119.922	"	Guano	Laura	" "	10. 1. 20.	Rodi
119.923	"	Capelluto	Sarah	" "	28. 11. 24.	Rodi
119.924	"	Maio Hasson	Sara	" "	25. 12. 20.	Rodi
119.925	"	Hasson	Bellina	" "	30. 3. 23.	Rodi
119.926	"	Da Fano	Giuseppina	" "	5. 5. 11.	Rodi
119.927	"	Capelluto	Matilde	" "	5. 5. 16.	Rodi
119.928	"	Hasson	Stella	" "	18. 1. 16.	Rodi
119.929	"	Hasson	Flora	"	22. 8. 27.	Rodi
119.930	"	Coen	Silvia	"	9. 1. 18.	Rodi
119.931	"	Franco	Lea	"	10. 3. 22.	Rodi
119.932	"	Israel	Giovanna	"	1. 4. 25.	Rodi
119.933	"	Capelluto	Zuzi	"	11. 4. 23.	Marseille
119.934	"	Varon	Laura	"	25. 6. 18.	Rodi
119.935	"	Capelluto Alh	Rebecca	"	11. 8. 19.	Roar
119.936	"	Sidis	Stella	"	13. 4. 20.	Rodi
119.937	"	Almeleh	Rachel	"	11. 2. 22.	Rodi
119.938	"	Benun	Stella	"	19. 8. 30.	Rodi
119.939	"	Alhadeff	Virginia	"	25. 10. 16.	Rodi
119.940	"	Kirsch	Maria	Polin.	28. 9. 12.	Chosanuw
119.941	"	Hasson	Elsa	Ital.	3. 5. 28	Rodi
119.942	"	Levi	Rachel	"	25. 12. 18.	Rodi
119.943	"	Israel	Susy	"	29. 5. 20.	Rodi
119.944	"	Avzaradel	Rosa	"	22. 4. 22.	Rodi
119.945	"	Alhadefe	Violetta	"	29. 11. 25.	Rodi
119.946	"	Ribak	Sarolta	D.R.	11. 1. 99.	Lackenbach
119.947	"	Avzaradel	Laura	Ital.	10. 4. 20.	Rodi
119.948	"	Surmani	Stella	"	25. 5. 24.	Rodi
119.949	"	Coen	Victoria	"	15. 3. 20.	Rodi

Excerpt from the admissions register of the Dachau concentration camp, October 27, 1944 with the name of the women from Rhodes NA, Washington

Subcamps and External Work Details of the Dachau Concentration Camp

During the second half of the war, the German economy became increasingly dependent on forced labor, including that of the concentration camp prisoners. Faced with a growing shortage of labor in the armaments industry, the SS began in 1942 to radically expand the exploitation of prisoner labor. In 1944, the number of prisoners in the Dachau concentration camp and its subcamps grew rapidly as a result of the deportations from the occupied countries, in particular due to the almost 40,000 Jews who arrived from the camps in the east. The majority of the some 100,000 prisoners deported to the Dachau concentration camp in 1944-1945 were sent to the subcamps.

The bunker construction site "Weingut I"
near Müldorf, 1944-1945.

StadtA Mühldorf am Inn

Beginning in 1940-1941, the SS increasingly assigned prisoners – mostly craftsmen and skilled workers – to work outside the Dachau camp grounds. They worked for a variety of SS institutions and on SS projects, including the building and maintenance of barracks, convalescent homes, hospitals and infirmaries, buildings for SS leaders and SS research projects. Prisoners had to defuse and remove bombs and clear debris following air raids. Concentration camp work details were stationed in Munich and Salzburg, where they cleaned up damage and performed construction work at various locations.

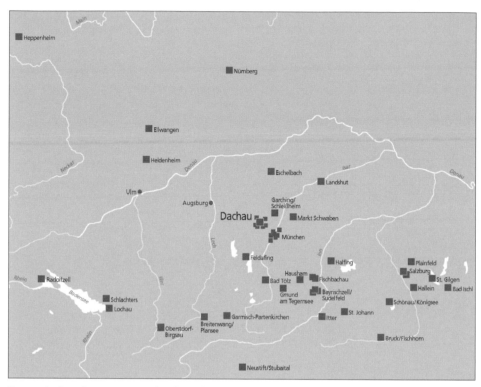

Not marked on the map: St. Lambrecht and Lind

Franz Przybylski (1910-1999) (center) and other prisoners defusing bombs at the Oberschleissheim airport near Munich, July 21, 1944

At the age of 29, Franz Przybylski was arrested as a member of the Polish Red Cross and deported to the Dachau concentration camp in April 1940. In 1944 he was assigned to the Stieler school bomb search and clearing work detail in Munich. He was forced to perform the life-threatening task of defusing bombs. Photo: SS, private ownership

Alpine hut with prisoners, May 1945
Photo: Andrzej Burzawa, KZ-Gst. Dachau

As of spring 1943, prisoners of the Dachau concentration camp had to perform forced labor for the aircraft industry, mostly manufacturing fighter planes. Prisoner accommodations were set up near the production sites.

Set the German shepherd on prisoners

We had a dreadful work detail leader. His name was Jäntsch – he had a German shepherd and every now and then he set the German shepherd on prisoners and when it had sunk its teeth into someone, he shouted "enough" and the dog pulled away … There [at the Sager & Woerner construction company in the BMW aircraft engine factory] I hauled iron and cement … It was very hard work. Then we unloaded cement and then we moved earth. We built bunkers, but not bunkers for shelter, not to protect people, but production bunkers, because there were air raids almost every day. Mannheimer, Erinnerungen

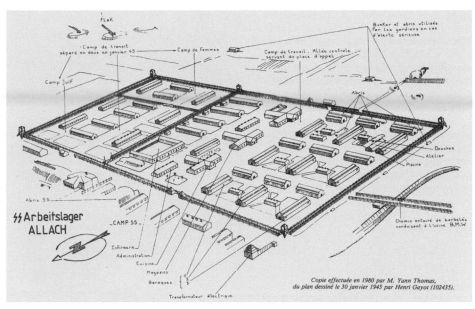

The Allach subcamp (BMW) The Allach subcamp was set up for the firm BMW (Bavarian Motor Works) in early 1943. The ca. 5,000 prisoners in the camp came from 18 different countries, primarily from the Soviet Union and France. They were forced to produce aircraft engines and carry out construction work under atrocious conditions. Amicale des Anciens de Dachau, Paris

Max Mannheimer was born in Moravia in 1920. In early 1943, the SS deported the Jewish family via the Theresienstadt "ghetto" to Auschwitz. Max Mannheimer survived numerous "selections". He was deported with his brother first to the Warsaw concentration camp and then to the Dachau subcamps at Karlsfeld and Mühldorf-Mettenheim in 1944. He was liberated there together with his brother Edgar on April 30, 1945. Photo: private ownership

Entrance area and gate of the Allach subcamp, 1945 Photo: after liberation, KZ-Gst. Dachau

Prisoners at the BMW factory in Allach measuring cylinders for airplane engines, undated. Photo: BMW, KZ-Gst. Dachau

As of early 1943, almost 3,000 prisoners were forced to work in the factories of the Messerschmitt AG in Augsburg. The prisoners worked in alternating twelve-hour shifts, manufacturing mainly fighter planes. As Allied air raids intensified from February 1944, hundreds of prisoners were killed because they were not allowed to seek protection in shelters. After the Haunstetten camp was destroyed in April 1944, the survivors were transferred to other camps in Augsburg. Excessive working hours and exhaustive marches to the work sites, poor and inadequate food, terrible hygiene, disease and harassment – these were the conditions under which the prisoners had to live and work in Augsburg.

Prisoners working in a hall of the Messerschmitt factory damaged by bombs, 1944
Photo: private ownership

Edmond Falkuss (b. 1916) emigrated with his parents in 1935 from the Saarland to France. In 1940, after the capitulation of France, he was arrested by the Gestapo and charged with treason. He was sent to the Dachau concentration camp in 1942. In 1943 he became camp clerk in the subcamps of the Messerschmitt AG in Augsburg. Photo: Ludwig Eiber, 2000, HdGB

Execution
The execution took place according to the following criteria: those who let themselves be hanged without causing any fuss, they received a noose around their necks. They were then pushed off a pedestal so that their neck broke immediately. But those, like the Russians for instance, who defended themselves or cursed the SS, they were hanged slowly. That meant that they were put on the pedestal and were hanged with great care so that they suffocated. And this process of suffocation took a long time. He would wriggle on the rope for a while, suffering terribly. Yes, that's how I saw some being hanged … fifteen, twenty or so.

Falkuss, eyewitness interview; Falkuss was in the Dachau concentration camp, 1942-1945 HdGB

The Haunstetten subcamp destroyed by bombs, 1944 Photo: private ownership

The Zeppelin airship construction company in Friedrichshafen maintained a subcamp from spring 1943. About 1,000 prisoners had to produce side panels and fuel tanks for V-2 rockets. The camp and production sites were destroyed by a series of air raids in 1944. Countless prisoners were killed. In September 1944, the remaining prisoners were distributed among the camps at Überlingen, Saulgau and Mittelbau-Dora.

V-2 rockets The V-2 rocket ("V" stood for "Vergeltung", vengeance) was one of the so-called miracle weapons that were supposed to break Allied superiority in 1944. The Zeppelin company was part of the team manufacturing the rocket. In Friedrichshafen and Saulgau mainly the mid-section rocket cases and fuel tanks were produced. BA-MA

Ivan Matijasic (b. 1916)
Dr. Ivan Matijasic was arrested in his hometown of Pazin in October 1943 because he had provided medical assistance to Yugoslav partisans. Via Trieste, he arrived in the Dachau concentration camp on January 16, 1944. In June 1944, he was taken to the subcamp at Saulgau, where he replaced the deceased prisoner doctor. When over 200 critically ill prisoners from Überlingen arrived at the camp in early April 1945, he was able to save many lives despite limited medical resources.
Photo: 1945 after liberation, Archive Ivan Matijasic

During the air raids on the factory, the SS men shot from their shelters at prisoners who ran out of the barracks towards the camp fence and tried to flee. Many prisoners were killed.

Stanislav Biedron, testimony given in 1979; Biedron was in the Friedrichshafen subcamp of the Dachau concentration camp, 1943-1945
BA Ludwigsburg

Production hall of the Zeppelin factory, undated
Concentration camp prisoners produced parts for the V-2 rocket in this hall. It was destroyed in mid-1944 by air raids. Photo: private ownership

The "final solution of the Jewish question" was carried out in many stages and at varying places. Most of the Jews in the occupied territories of the Soviet Union were killed in mass executions. In 1942-1943 the Jews in the Polish General Government were murdered in the extermination camps of Belzec, Treblinka and Sobibor. Jews from other Polish territories were either sent to the extermination camps Chelmno, Treblinka, Auschwitz and Majdanek, or shot. Jews from the Reich, occupied Europe, and, after the German occupation in March 1944, Hungary were transported to the "East" to be murdered, mainly in Auschwitz. At least six million people were murdered.

Deportation of residents of the Warsaw ghetto after the suppression of the uprising, April or May 1943 Żydowski Instytut Historyczny, Warsaw

Deportation of Jews from Siedlce/Poland to the Treblinka extermination camp, August 23, 1942 Photo: Hubert Pfoch, IfZ

Arrival of a transport of Jews from Hungary at the ramp of the Auschwitz-Birkenau camp, early summer 1944 Yad Vashem

As part of the so-called "Jäger Program", Jewish prisoners mainly from Hungary, Lithuania, Poland and Czechoslovakia were once again deported as forced laborers to the Dachau camp in summer 1944. Most of them were transferred to the Kaufering and Mühldorf subcamps. There the prisoners suffered severely under the very poor living conditions. Thousands died or were transported as "invalids" to be exterminated at Auschwitz.

The **"selection": women,** who were selected at the ramp of Auschwitz-Birkenau as workers, summer 1944. Yad Vashem

Szmuel Kuczinski (b. 1925) (far left) visiting the mass grave of the victims of the evacuation transport, in the 1950s. Although he lost a leg in an air raid, he was the only member of his family to survive. In 1944, he was deported from Auschwitz to Kaufering, together with his father Laib Leon Kuczinski (1906-1945). His father died in his arms. KZ-Gst. Dachau

Elchanan Elkes was a respected doctor and committed supporter of Jewish cultural life in Kaunas (Lithuania). In July 1944 he was transported from the Kaunas ghetto to the Kaufering subcamp. There he was active in the infirmary barrack. He died of an infection in October 1944. Elkes (left) in the Kaunas ghetto, between 1941 and 1944. Photo: Zvi Kadushin Col, Diaspora Museum

Chaim Glick (b. 1924) and **Chevach Glick** (b. 1905), father and son. Both were deported from the Kaunas ghetto in July 1944 to Kaufering (Chevach to camp I, Chaim to camp II). Chevah died shortly after liberation, his son survived. KZ-Gst. Dachau

Gisela Popper (b. 1914) was driven out of Hungary with thousands of other Jewish women on a five-day march to the German border in November 1944. From there the women were transported to the Dachau concentration camp in cattle cars. In the Kaufering XI subcamp, Gisela Popper first had to haul stones; she was later assigned to the camp office. During an air raid she managed to escape from an evacuation transport. Photo: private ownership

Since the beginning of 1944, Allied air attacks had destroyed large segments of the production capacity of the German aviation industry. To protect the production of fighter planes, the facilities were to be relocated into large bunkers or underground. A giant construction program, the so-called Jäger program, was to force a turning point in the aerial war. 100,000 Jewish prisoners were to build six giant bunkers in which 3,000 fighter planes could be assembled monthly. At Landsberg/Kaufering, Mühldorf and Überlingen, a total of 17 subcamps were established in which atrocious living conditions prevailed. The majority of the prisoners were Jews from Hungary and Lithuania, who, beginning in the summer of 1944, were deported as forced laborers to the Reich territory.

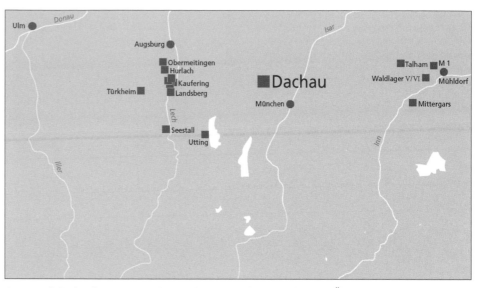

Camps of the bunker construction projects Not shown on the map: Überlingen

Request for concentration camp prisoners to be deployed in the bunker projects
Dear Himmler!
… At the same time, I request of you to place at my disposal the greatest possible number of concentration camp prisoners for aircraft production, since this workforce has proven itself to be very useful until now … The current situation of the aerial war makes it necessary to relocate industry underground. Precisely this connection allows an optimal concentration of the prisoners in camps and in work gangs… Yours, Göring, Reich Marshal of the Greater German Reich.

Telegram sent by Hermann Göring to Heinrich Himmler, February 15, 1944 (excerpt)
StA Nuremberg

Prisoners in front of the bunker construction site
The large bunker at Kaufering/Landsberg was to provide a bombproof production site for the jet fighter Messerschmitt 262, considered decisive for the war. However, it proved impossible to begin production before the end of the war. In the final phase of the war some prisoners wore civilian clothing. Crosses made of cloth or painted on their backs marked them as concentration camp prisoners. Photo: private ownership

Rail line to the bunker, undated
Photo: private ownership

To house the Jewish prisoners designated to perform forced labor in the construction of the large bunkers, eight primitive camps were set up in the environs of the towns Landsberg and Kaufering. An estimated 30,000 prisoners were deployed in Kaufering. More than 10,000 of them died from the strain of the work, from disease, and from the terrible living conditions in the camps

The Kaufering IV subcamp (Hurlach), 1945 In the last few weeks before liberation, Kaufering IV was declared a "sick camp." The sick prisoners were no longer sent to work, but neither were they provided any medical treatment. Essentially, they were left to themselves. Hundreds died in agony. Photo: US Army, April 28, 1945, NA Washington

Corpses found in the Kaufering IV camp (Hurlach), 1945 Photo: US Army, April/May 1945, KZ-Gst. Dachau

Viktor Nečas (1907-1991) (1941-1945 in the Dachau concentration camp) was one of the few non-Jewish prisoners in Kaufering. These prisoners were mostly entrusted with leadership functions. A veteran of the Spanish Civil War, Viktor Nečas was camp elder in the Kaufering III camp. He was able to save the camp records from destruction and took them with him to his home in Vienna. In 1973 he donated them to the Jewish Museum in New York. KZ-Gst. Dachau

Interior of an earthen hut at the Kaufering IV camp (Hurlach), 1945
Most of the prisoners were quartered in earthen huts. Although the huts were outfitted with ovens, there was usually a shortage of fuel. Some 50 to 60 prisoners slept in a hut. Rain, but above all the winter, made living conditions catastrophic. Photo: US Army, April 28, 1945, NA Washington

Clay pipe huts at the Kaufering VII camp, 1944-1945
The camps in the Kaufering/Landsberg area were extremely primitive. Only official barracks were built out of wood. The prisoners lived in tents, plywood structures, and earthen huts, or in so-called clay pipe huts. Round arches were formed out of clay pipes inserted into one another and covered with earth. The huts served mainly as accommodation for women in the Kaufering I, VII and XI camps. KZ-Gst. Dachau

…hardly any of those older than 24 or 25 managed to survive

After two or three days I was assigned to a work detail called the "Moll night shift" … The work was especially hard … mostly working with concrete, loading and unloading sacks of concrete, carrying rail tracks, unloading trains, mixing cement … we worked more or less in the dark. We had to work constantly and as quickly as possible, the guards were from the Organization Todt, mostly vicious, some even cruel … hardly any of the elder [prisoners], i.e. those older than 24 or 25, managed to survive.

Ervin-Deutsch, Night Shift in Work Camp III; he was in the Dachau concentration camp, 1944-1945.

Night shift

We, those who entered the entrance gates of the Landsberg concentration camp [Kaufering], believed that nothing more could horrify us … But when we were told that the detail we belonged to was to work in a night shift beginning the following day, the blood froze in our veins.
In the winter of 1944 almost all of the 4,000 prisoners in Landsberg No. 1 as well as those in Kaufering No. 3 and No. 4 worked in the Mohl woods, building an underground factory. Roll call with its endless beatings took place at dusk. The trip [to the site], across a bitterly cold frost, through snow, through knee-deep snow, lasted a few hours. Weakened, we reached the woods. We shivered from cold, from hunger and from exhaustion. That was only the beginning of the torture. We worked out in the open with hardly any light. People fell from the scaffolding, froze in the snow, fell into an abyss unnoticed. They were first looked for early in the morning, as their absence was noticed at the roll call preceding our return.

Lustig, Concentration Camp Dictionary; he was in the Dachau concentration camp, 1944-1945.

Prisoners from Kaufering during their evacuation march to Dachau, Landsberg April 24, 1945
Photo: Johann Mutter (illegally taken private photo), STadtA Landsberg am Lech

Only a few days before the arrival of the American troops, the Kaufering prisoners were marched off or transported with trains in the direction of Dachau. Only those prisoners who were unfit to be transported remained behind. Many prisoners died of exhaustion, were shot by guards, or lost their lives during air raids.

Prisoners performing excavation work, 1944-1945 In twelve hour shifts the prisoners had to do mainly construction and transport work. Photo: Private ownership (Neuhaus/Fenner)

The camp complex established from mid-1944 near Mühldorf am Inn was comprised of the camps M1 at Mettenheim, the forest camps V and VI at Ampfing and the camps Thalham and Mittergars. The greater majority of the more than 8,000 male and female prisoners were Hungarian Jews, who came to Mühldorf mainly via Auschwitz.

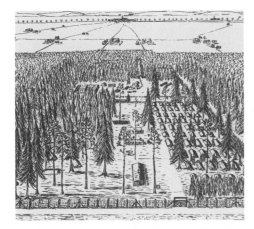

The forest camps V/VI, drawing based on site remains and evidence given by witnesses, 1981
The some 2,000 prisoners of the forest camps, among them 50 women, lived in earthen huts and so-called "fin" tents. Besides the subcamps belonging to the concentration camp system, there were also forest camps for civilian forced laborers from abroad. Drawing: private ownership

The bunker construction site "Weingut I", 1944-1945 The giant bunker was supposed to be 400 meters long and 85 meters wide. By the end of the war, seven arch elements, each of which was 33 meters long and 35 meters high, had been completed. The prisoners had to transport building materials and cement, lay tracks, and move earth. Festschrift, Polensky & Zöllner, 1955

"Fin tents" at forest camp V, 1945
In the "summer camp" the prisoners were housed in tents or huts. These were without windows and were mainly made of plywood. They were unsuitable for use in winter.
Photo: taken after liberation, NA Washington

Earthen huts at forest camp V, 1945
Earthen huts were built for the so-called winter camp. Covered with earth, they offered a certain protection against frost as long as no water penetrated them. Around 30 prisoners lived in an earthen hut. Photo: taken after liberation, NA Washington

In the summer of 1944, some 800 prisoners were transferred from the Dachau subcamps Friedrichshafen and Germering, which had been destroyed by bombs, to Überlingen. There they had to dig a tunnel system into the cliffs along the shores of Lake Constance near Überlingen-Goldbach for the firm "Magnesit". The Goldbach tunnels were to serve as a bombproof underground location for the Friedrichshafen industrial facilities, mainly for the firms Zeppelin and Dornier.

Entrance to the Goldbach tunnel in Überlingen, 1946 Fotoarchiv Lauterwasser, Überlingen

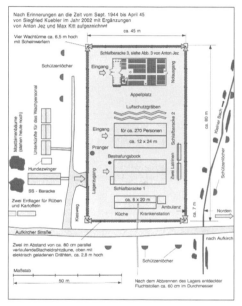

The Überlingen subcamp,
sketch by Anton Jež Sketch: private ownership

Anton Jež (b. 1925) joined a national liberation movement in 1941 that fought first against the Italian and then against the German occupation of Slovenia. In February 1944 he was arrested by the local police and after spending two months in prison was handed over to the Germans. They deported him to Dachau in April 1944. He was subjected to forced labor in the Neuaubing, Gemering and Überlingen subcamps.

Photo: private ownership

The tunnel
The tunnel was our misfortune and our luck at the same time. Our misfortune because we worked under extremely difficult conditions and without safety precautions. Constant collapses of the ceiling resulted in serious injuries and also dead victims on the spot. … Luck, our luck was that we spent most of the winter under the earth's surface. This was the saving of many of us, lightly clothed and undernourished. Jež, The Tunnel

Human Experiments, Murder and Resistance

Fatal medical experiments on prisoners were conducted mainly for the German Air Force. Prisoners deemed unfit for work were either murdered through injections or deported to the extermination camps. Despite the worst possible living conditions in the camp, many lives were saved in Dachau thanks to solidarity among the prisoners and secret acts of resistance.

During the war concentration camp prisoners were abused in murderous experiments for military medicine. The most important for the military authorities included malaria experiments, "biochemical" and sulfanilamide experiments, and aeronautic medical experiments for research into means of survival at great altitudes or in marine distress.

High altitude experiments

The development of jet aircraft capable of ascending to great altitudes confronted air force medical authorities with the question as to how people could work under such conditions and how they might be rescued if there was a sudden drop in pressure. More than 70 prisoners lost their lives in the course of these experiments.

Photo series, taken by an SS doctor during the altitude experiments, 1942
A fatal experiment on the formation of embolus in the brain was conducted on ten Jewish prisoners.
NA Washington

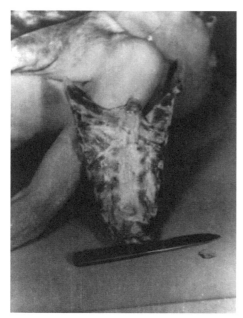

Post-mortem of an experimental subject
KZ-Gst. Dachau

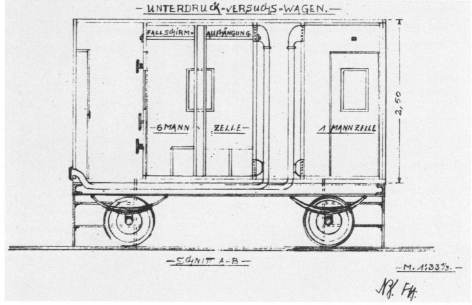

Mobile pressure chamber, drawing by an unknown prisoner, undated
Musiol, Dachau 1933-1945

Hypothermia experiments
Many pilots shot down over the ocean died in the icy waters. In August 1942, the Air Force launched a series of human experiments to identify possibilities for rescue. Almost 90 prisoners died in the process.

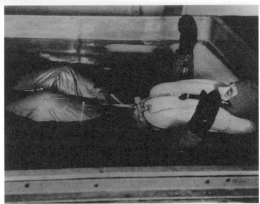

Photo series, taken by SS doctors during the hypothermia experiments, 1942 KZ-Gst. Dachau

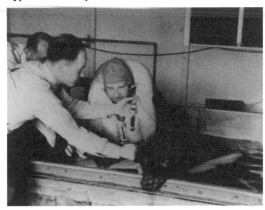

Exitus					
Versuch Nr.	Wasser-temperatur	Körper-temperatur bei Entfernung aus dem Wasser	Körper-temperatur beim Eintritt des Todes	Verweildauer im Wasser	Eintritt des Todes
5	5,2°	27,7°	27,7°	66'	66'
13	6°	29,2°	29,2°	80'	87'
14	4°	27,8°	27,5°	95'	100'
16	4°	28,7°	26°	60'	74'
23	4,5°	27,8°	25,7°	57'	65'
25	4,5°	27,8°	26,6°	51'	65'
	4,2°	26,7°	25,9°	53'	53'

Eine Darstellung Dr. Raschers über 7 tödlich verlaufene Unterkühlungsversuche

"Exitus" table (exitus means death) The table gives the temperature of the ice bath, the body temperatures upon removal and at death, length of time in the bath, and the total time until death. StA Nuremberg

Malaria experiments began in February 1942 in connection with the planned settlement of the southern regions of the Soviet Union by German colonists. The experiments were conducted until March 1945.

Professor Dr. Claus Schilling, the over 70-year-old former head of the Department of Tropical Diseases at the Robert Koch Institute in Berlin, presided over the experiments. He infected some 1,100 persons with malaria, among whom were 185 clergymen, 176 Poles, four Czechs and five Germans.
KZ-Gst. Dachau

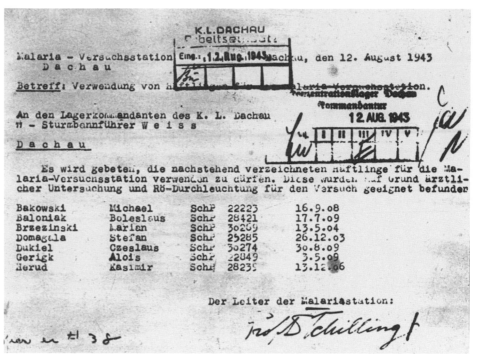

Letter from Claus Schilling, the head of the malaria station, to the camp commandant, requesting new experimental subjects, August 12, 1943 Musiol, Dachau 1933-1945

Experiments with medicines
In keeping with Himmler's dilettantish fantasies, a universal medicine was to be developed; in the form of "biochemical" tablets, this was to be a German medical breakthrough equivalent to that of penicillin. In the summer of 1942, the relevant experiments began in Dachau. Prisoners were injected with pus and subsequently treated with "biochemical" tablets or a new kind of sulfanilamide.

Kazimierz Majdański, later an archbishop in Poland, survived as young chaplain the biochemical experiments with the help of prisoner orderlies, who were able to save him through a secret injection of Tibatin. Photo: Majdański, Zeugen.

The catastrophic results of the "biochemical" experiments
All sepsis cases were ad Exitum. (...) In conclusion it needs to be said that of a total number of 40 cases one positive case and four cases that can with reservations be considered positive contrast with 35 failures, 10 of which ended fatally. The tests in Dachau will be continued with ...

Interim report by Prof. Ernst-Robert Grawitz, SS Reich doctor, on the experiments in the Dachau concentration camp, submitted to Himmler, August 29, 1942

Overall, "biochemical" experiments were conducted on 90 prisoners. These included forty clergy, six Jewish and ten criminal prisoners. Twenty-nine prisoners died in immense agony.

Seawater-drinking experiments

In order to ascertain survival chances when drinking seawater during emergencies at sea, experiments were conducted on 40 Sinti and Roma in summer 1944.

But Beiglböck was pitiless

Subjectively the patients suffered from a nagging hunger and, above all, a horrific thirst that only became worse by drinking seawater. This thirst was so terrible that some patients did not shy away from drinking the dirty water used for washing the floor! I saw one of these poor devils crawling on his knees begging in vain for water. But Beiglböck was pitiless.

Sworn statement by the prisoner orderly Ignaz Bauer (1944-1945 in the Dachau concentration camp) for the Nuremberg Doctors' Trial, 1946 StA Nuermberg

The experiments were extremely cruel, even if no prisoner died during these experiments.

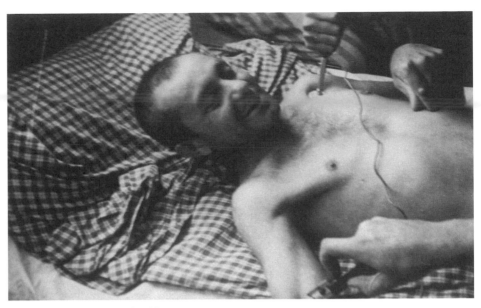

Photo of an experimental subject,
August 1944 USHMM

Karl H. (1914-1984)

Karl H., a Sinto from Munich, was deported to the Auschwitz extermination camp in March 1943. He was one of the few Sinti who survived Auschwitz. In early August 1944 he was sent to the Buchenwald concentration camp. There he was selected with other Sinti for the seawater experiments at the Dachau concentration camp. The Sinti were divided into four groups: one was to receive no food or water, another was given only pure seawater to drink, a third received seawater with a taste additive, and the fourth chemically desalinated water. Karl H., who belonged to the third group, survived the experiments, which lasted up to 12 days. He testified about this crime at the Nuremberg Doctors' Trial.

Dr. Wilhelm Beiglböck (1905-1963)
Beiglböck was the doctor responsible for the seawater-drinking experiments. Bayle, Croix gammée

Karl H. (right) with his sister Rosa and his uncle Rudolf H. on the way to the October Fest in Munich, around 1930 DZ Sinti und Roma, Heidelberg

The euthanasia program codenamed "14 f 13" program ended in 1942 in Dachau. But in the infirmary those deemed "unfit for work" were still "selected" at intervals of roughly three months. They were murdered by injection, simply left to die in the invalid barracks, or they were deported to the extermination camps.

The killing of the "mentally ill"

Mentally ill persons were regularly killed by injection in the Dachau concentration camp until the war ended.

I can furthermore remember that on around April 24, 1945, Dr. Hintermaier brought 18 young men, who were visibly mentally ill or had had their sense taken out them in other ways, to the crematorium and killed them there by injection.

Sworn statement by Emil Mahl, the former capo at the crematorium. Dachau Trial, exhibit 93

Killing through phenol injections in the bunker

Beginning in 1943, prisoners suffering from TB were murdered in groups of 20 by injection in the bunker.

The injections were given in the bunker in a cell close to the guard room, and I collected the corpses myself and brought them to the crematorium. With the first 20, the corpses lay in two or three different cells, the rest lay in one large heap in one single cell.

Prisoner account by the former head orderly Heinrich Stöhr KZ-Gst. Dachau

The invalid camp Lublin-Majdanek On January 3, 1944, a transport with 1,000 "invalids" was sent from the Dachau concentration camp to Majdanek. They were to die there of starvation and cold. According to details given by Zofia Leszińska, 469 of them had died by April 8, 1944.
Photo: interior view of a barrack in the Majdanek concentration camp after liberation, Muzeum Majdanek

Transports to the gas chambers in Auschwitz
Between September 25 and October 31, 1944, four transports with a total of 2,137 Jewish prisoners no longer able to work were sent from the Kaufering and Mühldorf subcamps to the gas chambers at Auschwitz.

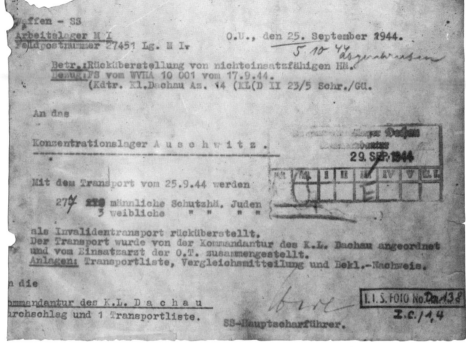

The "invalid camp" Bergen-Belsen
On December 21, 1944, a transport with 1,400 "invalids" was sent from Dachau to Bergen-Belsen. Between February 1945 and liberation on April 15, 1945, over 30,000 persons died of typhus there.

Photo: Bergen-Belsen concentration camp after liberation, IWM

Copy of a communiqué sent from the Dachau concentration camp to the Auschwitz concentration camp about a transport with prisoners unfit for work, September 25, 1944 ITS

Besides the mass shootings of Soviet prisoners of war in 1941-1942, numerous "special treatment" executions of non-inmates were carried out in the Dachau concentration camp. The victims were mainly persons sent by the Gestapo and thus not registered in the camp documents. How many were executed is not known. It is estimated that it must have been several hundred. Also covered by the category "special treatment" were executions of Dachau prisoners, mostly for "sabotage".

Executions

In the night of April 21 [1943], 22 civilians were shot, including three women. The reason why is not known, not even their origin could be established. In the night to April 18 the same fate befell an 18-year-old Ukrainian ...

On Thursday, May 6, four Yugoslav partisans were shot ...

Since May 23, three new gallows stand next to the crematorium. On May 26 ... a young Russian was executed. Nobody knows why.
Journal entries of Karel Kašák.

In the crematorium area Soviet officers were executed, shot in the head.
Photo: after liberation, KZ-Gst. Dachau

Execution of 31 Soviet air-force officers, who had escaped from the Moosburg POW camp. They were executed on February 22, 1944 near the crematorium, by shots in the head.

Execution of 92 Soviet officers
On September 4, 1944, 90 Soviet officers, members of the resistance group "Bratskoe Sotrudničestvo voennoplennych" (BSV – Brotherhood of Prisoners of War), were shot in the crematorium. On the following day, two officers incapable of walking were also shot.

Noor-un-nisa Inayat Khan (1913-1944)
The Indian princess Noor-un-nisa worked for the British Secret Service, SOE. She was arrested by the Gestapo in occupied Paris. Together with three other SOE agents, Yvonne Beekman, Elaine Plewman and Madeleine Damermant, she was shot in the crematorium area in September 1944. KZ-Gst. Dachau

Pjotr Fomin (1906-1944), one of those murdered. KZ-Gst. Dachau

Captain Michail Zinger (1886-1944), one of those shot.
Brodski, živyje Borjutsja.

In the course of the war, the prisoner transports served primarily to meet the constant need of the armaments industry for labor. Depending on actual requirements or the transporting of those persons no longer capable of working, the prisoners were transported back and forth between concentration camps. Due to the chaos of war, these transports took a long time to reach their destination. Many prisoners starved, died of thirst or suffocated in the boarded-up freight cars.

Living corpses

In the night of November 19 [1942], an invalid transport arrived at Dachau, the likes of which the Dachau prisoners had yet to lay eyes on … All of the cars were boarded shut with long nails so that every one of the 350 unfortunates had been without food, without air, without the chance to relieve themselves for a full eight days on the way from the Stutthof camp near Danzig to Dachau. … Living corpses is an inadequate description. … Of the 350, 57 dead were carried out of the cars, including three who were gnawed and cut on their upper arms and thighs down to the bone.

Journal entry by Karel Kašák

Transport, drawing by Vlastimir Kopač Muzej novejše zgodovine Slovenije, Ljubljana

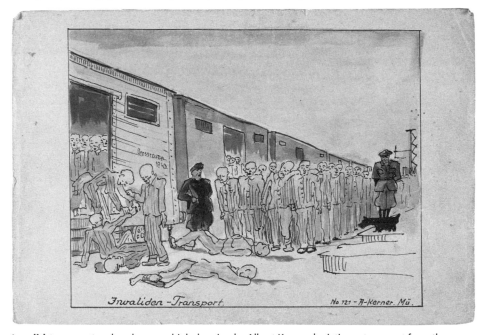

Invalid transport, colored pen-and-ink drawing by Albert Kerner depicting a transport from the Gross-Rosen concentration camp, 1945 KZ-Gst. Dachau

Resistance was immensely difficult and dangerous in the concentration camps. It existed nevertheless, undertaken by small groups or individuals and without the usual organizational structures. Solidarity among the prisoners saved the lives of many, and the dividing line between solidarity and resistance was often fluid.

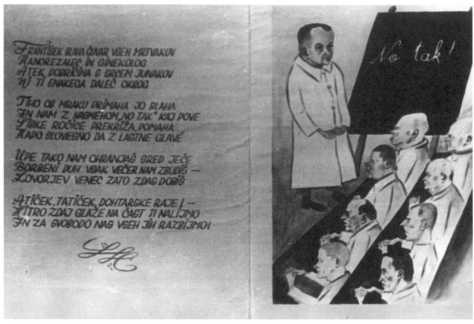

František Bláha The Czech doctor František Bláha – he was the first prisoner artist sent to the infirmary in 1942 – was forced to work as a corpsebearer there. In this despised function he had access to all places where persons died and could provide medical help and compassion. He was able to save many lives.
Drawing with a dedication from the prisoner doctors.
KZ-Gst. Dachau

Heinrich Stöhr Working as head orderly in the infirmary, the German prisoner Heinrich Stöhr saved the lives of many prisoners of various nationalities, at great risk to his own life.
Archive des Bayerischen Landtags, Munich

Josef Lauscher The Austrian Josef Lauscher was one of the most prominent members of the Communist prisoner community. As camp runner he used his wide network of contacts to help his fellow prisoners. He also tried to maintain contacts between the German-speaking and foreign Communists. Photo: private ownership

Karl Wagner Karl Wagner was one of the leading Communists in the Dachau concentration camp. Due to his bravery and humanity he enjoyed the respect of his fellow prisoners. He risked serious punishment as he refused to whip fellow prisoners at the Allach subcamp in his function as camp elder. KZ-Gst. Dachau

Illegal radio set that was hidden in the morgue DÖW

Edgar Kupfer-Koberwitz The writer Edgar Kupfer-Koberwitz worked as a clerk in the detail assigned to the firm Präzifix. Beginning in 1942 he was able to keep a journal as well as note down his past experiences. He hid the manuscript, which if discovered would have meant certain death, in the storage compound. He published his notes and journal entries in three volumes. Kupfer-Koberwitz, Dachau journals

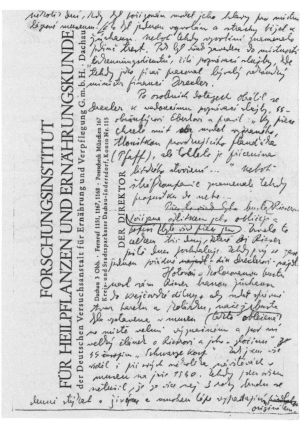

The secret journal entries of Karel Kašák

The Czech journalist Karel Kašák, who worked as a botanic painter at the plantation, kept a journal from 1940 to 1945. He fixed the entries bit by bit into the wall of the boiler house. In this way Kašák was able to store away 1,700 paper cards. KZ-Gst. Dachau

Hans Carls The clergyman Hans Carls, director of the Catholic Caritas charity in Wuppertal, collected documents for a planned book on the Dachau concentration camp and sent them secretly to Wuppertal. When the letter fell into Gestapo hands, he was incarcerated in the bunker in December 1943 for the spreading of "atrocity propaganda". Against all expectation, he was neither beaten to death nor executed there. KZ-Gst. Dachau

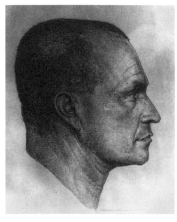

Rudolf Císař After the outbreak of the typhus epidemic at the beginning of 1943, Císař established contact to his resistance group RUDA in Bohemia. This group sent a large amount of medical supplies and a camera to the camp. Helped by Maria Weber, a civilian employee on the "plantation", Císař smuggled reports, documents and undeveloped films to Prague. Drawing by Joris Lebeau, Dachau 1944 KZ-Gst. Dachau

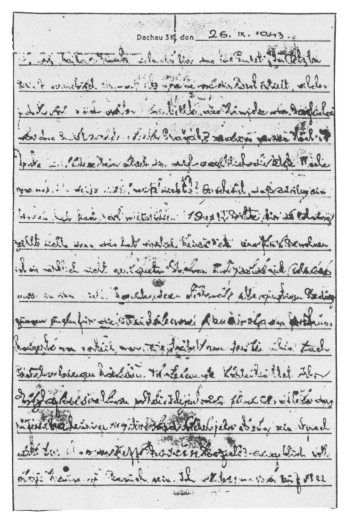

Letter by Rudolf Císař to his sister on September 26, 1943. Between the lines he wrote with invisible ink that became visible only after chemical treatment. KZ-Gst. Dachau

Wording: "Dear Majčička, on 9.22 some 1,900 Italians arrived … They raise their right arm even here – these idiots. Yesterday they brought around 120 Germans here, direct from the front. Where they were sent on to from here, I don't know. On the 19th some 60 train cars arrived with goods plundered in Italy, among it all lots of ladies' fabrics … Was the manifest sent this time to Moscow as well as Vlasta and Šeník ? Have you printed some fliers and newspapers? Do you have the camera that I wrote to you about? And the typewriter and printer from Karlín? … I wrote a letter to Mirek on Sunday, has he received it? It was black and then on Tuesday on white paper in the package with edelweiss. Your Ruda kisses you."

The Last Months and the Liberation

The last months were the most terrible. Countless prisoners were murdered on the evacuation marches. A severe typhus epidemic broke out in the incredibly overfilled Dachau concentration camp. The American liberators found the camp in a catastrophic state.

Dead prisoners in the crematorium after liberation

In summer 1944, the SS began to evacuate the first concentration camps as the advancing front approached. The roads were lined with the corpses of executed prisoners after the prisoner columns passed. Thousands of prisoners, ill or unable to walk, were murdered prior to evacuation.

Railway transports In freezing cold weather the prisoners were transported in open coal cars. Some trains were forced to turn around and shuttle back and forth between the overcrowded concentration camps that refused to accept the prisoners. Evacuation transport from Auschwitz at Kolín in Bohemia, January 24, 1945 Photo: Jindřich Kremer, Muzeum Auschwitz-Birkenau, Oswiecim

The death marches from the Auschwitz concentration camp (January 1945) Mass grave near Ćwiklice (Poland) of prisoners from Auschwitz murdered during an evacuation march, 1945 Muzeum Auschwitz-Birkenau, Oswiecim

The prisoners called out for water. An SS man shot into the rail car, and with a wooden club the capo beat the wounded until they were dead. Some wounded prisoners were thrown into cars full of corpses and an SS man trampled the living down so that they would not fall out of the full car.
Report from the Czech railway station Kolín.
In: Malá/Kubátová, Pochody smrti

Murder of those unable to walk

From February 1945, the SS began to murder the prisoners who were unable to walk. According to incomplete reports, the following persons were murdered:

– in the Ravensbrück concentration camp some 4,000-5,000 women in an improvised gas chamber;

– in the Sachsenhausen concentration camp some 4,000 prisoners were gassed or shot in the head;

– in the Mauthausen concentration camp 1,424 prisoners were gassed and an unknown number killed by other means;

– in the Gusen camp, a subcamp of Mauthausen, 890 prisoners were gassed under improvised conditions; on April 23, 1945, a further 600 prisoners were beaten to death with axes and truncheons.

Atrocities committed during later evacuation transports During the evacuation of the Stutthof concentration camp, the workforce of a Jewish subcamp was taken to the sea and shot on the beach. 1,016 prisoners from the Mittelbau-Dora and Neuengamme concentration camps were burned alive in a barn near Gardelegen.

The charred corpses of prisoners in the barn near Gardelegen, April 1945   MRD Besançon

Liberation of the Buchenwald and Bergen-Belsen concentration camps,
April 11 and 15, 1945
In Buchenwald and, above all, in Bergen-Belsen the Allies found thousands of dead and dying people. The reports and the photographs from the liberators caused revulsion and outrage around the world.

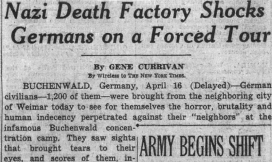

Nazi Death Factory Shocks Germans on a Forced Tour

By GENE CURRIVAN
By Wireless to The New York Times.

BUCHENWALD, Germany, April 16 (Delayed)—German civilians—1,200 of them—were brought from the neighboring city of Weimar today to see for themselves the horror, brutality and human indecency perpetrated against their "neighbors" at the infamous Buchenwald concentration camp. They saw sights that brought tears to their eyes, and scores of them, including German nurses, just fainted away.

They saw more than 20,000 nondescript prisoners, many of them barely living, who were all that remained of the normal complement of 80,000. The Germans were able to evacuate the others before we overran the place on April 10.

There were 32,705 that the "vis-

Continued on Page 8, Column 5

ARMY BEGINS SHIFT TO PACIFIC FRONT

Some Supplies Diverted in U. S., Others Sent From Europe—War Output Still High

By SIDNEY SHALETT

The "New York Times" report on the liberation of the Buchenwald concentration camp, April 18, 1945.

The second phase of the evacuation

When in April 1945 the division of Germany loomed, Himmler laid down the evacuation routes for the remaining concentration camps. The prisoners from the northern part of Germany were to be moved to the Baltic and North Sea coasts, obviously to be drowned. The prisoners from the southern part were to be assembled in the Alps, where the SS wanted to resist the Allies.

No prisoner is to fall into enemy hands alive

Surrender is out of the question. The camp is to be evacuated immediately. No prisoner is to fall into enemy hands alive. The prisoners behaved atrociously towards the civilian population in Buchenwald.

Heinrich Himmler on April 18, 1945, answering an inquiry whether the Flossenbürg concentration camp could be surrendered to the enemy. KZ-Gst. Dachau

Victim of the death march after the evacuation of Sachsenhausen ACICR

The burning Cap Arcona shortly after being attacked, May 3, 1945
7,000 prisoners from Neuengamme and Stutthof concentration camps, and many hundreds from the subcamps of Mittelbau-Dora were transported out onto the open sea on the ships Cap Arcona and Thielbeck. There they were mistakenly sunk by the RAF. IWM

To sink them on open seas

On April 18, I received an order to load them [the prisoners] on barges and to bring the barges to the Baltic or North Sea via the Spree canal and to sink them on open seas.

Statement given by Anton Kaindl, the Sachsenhausen camp commandant, at the Sachsenhausen trial, 1947.

Unable to assemble enough barges, Kaindl had the prisoners march towards Lübeck. They were liberated partly by the Soviet Army, partly by the U.S. Army Todeslager Sachsenhausen

At the end of 1944, the overcrowding of the camp became even more extreme. More and more emaciated prisoners arrived at the camp with the evacuation transports. The hygienic conditions and the supplies of food rations became catastrophic. In November a typhus fever epidemic broke out that claimed thousands of lives.

Food situation

The food is still very bad – just water and [more] water. – And for days now it has also been unsalted. Kupfer-Koberwitz, Dachau journals

The **Slovenian Stane Šinkovec** (b. 1923) was arrested by the Gestapo in 1942 because of resistance activities and transferred to the Dachau concentration camp. At first he was sent to the penal block and then abused in malaria experiments. During the typhus epidemic at the beginning of 1945, he volunteered for the dangerous work of caring for those suffering from the disease. KZ-Gst. Dachau

Prisoners in an overfilled barrack after liberation.
Up to 500 prisoners were crowded into a barrack room built for 50 persons. USHMM

Everywhere the stench of rotting corpses

Along the barrack road lay a lot of dead prisoners who had died on the same day and were yet to be taken to the crematorium ... Everywhere the stench of rotting corpses and excrement. This stench mixed with the smell of burnt human flesh from the nearby crematorium. Šinkovec, Dachau Zbornik.

In April 1945, the prisoners – initially within their individual national groups – joined together to counter the looming danger of liquidation. In the infirmary, whose personnel came from different nations, the foundations for an international camp leadership were laid.

The international resistance group in the infirmary
The core of the future International Dachau Committee consisted of the Belgians Arthur Haulot and Albert Guérisse, the Pole Kazimierz Maliszewski, the Frenchman Edmond Michelet and the Albanian Ali Kuci.
Photo: Arthur Haulot (center), KZ-Gst. Dachau

The Communist group
A group of Communist functionary prisoners was assembled around the camp elder Oskar Müller, shown here in a photo taken shortly after liberation. KZ-Gst. Dachau

"Self-protection"
On April 24, the SS camp leadership raised a so-called auxiliary police made up of German and a few foreign prisoners, who were marked by a white armband with the letters "H.P." (Hilfs-polizist - auxiliary policeman). The prisoners secretly produced more of these armbands and distributed them to reliable fellow prisoners. Camouflaged in this way, these prisoners then held watch at night so as to preempt any liquidation attempts by the SS.

Illegal armband of the auxiliary police from Stanislav Zámežník KZ-Gst. Dachau

Revolt in the town of Dachau on April 28, 1945
On April 28, 1945, an armed revolt broke out in the town of Dachau. Both former and escaped concentration camp prisoners, and a renegade Volkssturm (civilian militia) company took part. At around 8:30 am the rebels occupied the Town Hall. The superior forces of the SS bloodily suppressed the revolt within a few hours.

Georg Scherer
The organizer of the revolt was the Dachau citizen Georg Scherer, a former Dachau inmate who had served as camp elder in 1940.

Holzhaider, Die Sechs vom Rathausplatz

Karl Riemer's mission
Karl Riemer (a prisoner in the Dachau concentration camp since 1933) fled from the camp on April 26, 1945. He succeeded in crossing the front lines, some 50 kilometers away, by April 29. The American town commandant in Pfaffenhofen assured him immediate help for the prisoners in the Dachau concentration camp. It was not yet known in Pfaffenhofen that the order to liberate the camp had already been given that very same morning.

KZ-Gst. Dachau

Those who died during the revolt:

Fritz Dürr spent many years as a prisoner in the Dachau camp, and was executed after the suppression of the revolt.

Anton Hackl a Dachau prisoner and Spanish Civil War veteran from Austria, died fighting against the SS.

Erich Hubmann a Dachau prisoner and Spanish Civil War veteran from Austria, died fighting against the SS.

Hans Pflügler worker from Dachau, took part in the revolt as a civilian, and was executed.

Anton Hechtl farmer from Schönberg, took part in the revolt as a member of the Volkssturm, and was executed.

Lorenz Scherer farmer from Schwabhausen, took part in the revolt as a member of the Volkssturm, and was executed.

With defeat looming it became increasingly important to the SS to remove evidence of the crimes they committed in the concentration camps. At the Dachau concentration camp they began with the destruction of incriminating evidence in April 1945. In addition, plans for murdering the prisoners were worked out under the codenames "Wolke A I" ["Cloud A I"] and "Wolkenbrand" ["Cloud fire"], which, however, were never carried out. The first preparations for evacuating the camp began in mid-April. The prisoners were to be evacuated in the direction of Tyrol. On April 26, over 10,000 prisoners were forced to leave the Dachau concentration camp on foot, in trains, or in trucks. The largest group of some 7,000 prisoners was driven southward on a foot-march lasting several days. More than 1,000 prisoners did not survive this "death march". Overall, the evacuation transports cost many thousands of prisoners their lives.

Murdered prisoners from the Kaufering IV subcamp along the rail line Kaufering-Landsberg
Photo: US Army, NA Washington

...shattering their skulls with rifle-butts
Arduously the endless gray line of prisoners crept over the mountainous terrain. Shots were fired again and again. Finally we reached Bad Tölz. Our guard units were now so nervous that they did not even shy away from cold-blooded murder under the eyes of the civilians. Our comrades fell completely exhausted onto the cobblestones, onto the sidewalk, onto the steps of the houses. And the heartless murderers ... did not shrink back from, in the middle of the extremely busy town, shooting the comrades in the neck or ... shattering their skulls with rifle-butts.

Riemer, Fall into the Dark; Riemer was in the Dachau concentration camp, 1944-1945

Dachau prisoners marching through Bad Tölz, early May 1945 Archiv Tölzer Kurier

Chronology of the final weeks March-April 1945

Over 20,000 prisoners from the concentration camps Natzweiler, Buchenwald and Flossenbürg as well as numerous Dachau external work details and subcamps were crammed into the Dachau main camp and the Allach subcamp.

April 4 Danish and Norwegian prisoners are handed over to the International Red Cross and taken to Sweden.

April 9 The Hitler-assassin Georg Elser is shot at the crematorium on orders from Berlin.

April 17 and 24-27 The "special" prisoners gathered at the Dachau concentration camp are transported to Tyrol.

April 19 The French General Charles Delestraint is shot next to the crematorium.

April 23 Work details no longer leave the camp.

April 26 The prisoner Karl Riemer flees in order to get help from American troops. Around 7,000 prisoners are forced on a "death march" towards the Alps.

April 27 Victor Maurer, an International Red Cross representative, arrives at the camp.

April 28 The Dachau town uprising. The last members of the SS camp leadership leave Dachau, command is handed over to SS Unter-sturmführer Heinrich Wicker. The secretly formed International Prisoners Committee takes over the control of prisoner camp during the night.

April 29 The Dachau concentration camp is liberated by troops of the U.S. Army.

Prisoners on an evacuation march from the Kaufering subcamps to Dachau at Landsberg am Lech, end of April 1945 StadtA Landsberg am Lech Around 7,000 prisoners were evacuated from the Kaufering camps and sent on marches in the direction of Dachau.

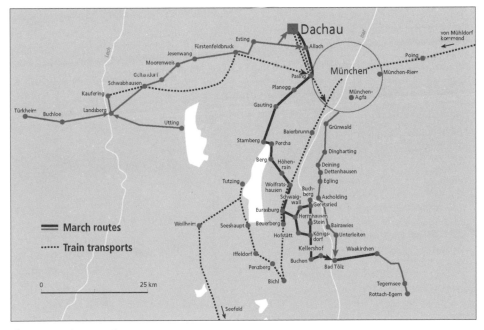

The evacuation marches Wagner, Karte Todesmarsch.

After the old SS camp command and the guard units had cleared out, another SS unit assumed guard over the prisoners' camp on April 28, 1945. On the same day Victor Maurer, a representative of the International Red Cross, negotiated an agreement to surrender the camp to U.S. troops. The U.S. troops received the order to take over the Dachau concentration camp on April 29. An advance commando from the 7th Army under Brigadier General Henning Linden (42nd Infantry Division "Rainbow"), accompanied by some journalists, officially accepted the surrender at the gate to the SS camp from the acting commandant Heinrich Wicker. At around the same time, members of the 45th Infantry Division "Thunderbird", under the leadership of Lt. Col. Felix L. Sparks, had advanced to the SS camp from the west. Here they came across a train full of corpses. Gunfire was exchanged with SS units and members of the SS were executed. Both U.S. units met in front of the gatehouse. Having waited in unbearable tension and despair, the cheering prisoners now streamed out to greet their liberators.

As we approached the camp the first thing we came to was a railroad track leading out of the camp with a lot of open box cars on it. As we crossed the tracks we looked back into the cars, and the most horrible sight I have ever seen ... met my eyes. The cars were loaded with dead bodies. Most of them were naked and all of them were skin and bones... Many of them had bullet holes in the back of their heads. It made us sick at our stomachs and so mad we could do nothing but clench our fists...

Letter by Lt. Bill Cowling to his family, depicting his impressions of the liberation of the camp, April 28-30, 1945 Linden, Surrender

Soldiers from the 157th Infantry Regiment of the U.S. Army under the command of Felix Sparks during the take over of the camp, April 29, 1945 Photo: Arland B. Musser, USHMM

Dead prisoners in the "death train" from Buchenwald, April 29, 1945
Photo: Arland B. Musser, NA Washington

Execution in the coalyard, April 29, 1945
Some American soldiers were so embittered by the sight of the death train that they began to execute captured SS men. The commander of the battalion, Felix L. Sparks, saw what was happening and stopped the execution immediately. Overall, some 50 members of the SS were killed during liberation.
Photo: Arland B. Musser, NA Washington

But where are the Americans?
The news that the SS command has moved out, that the white flag is flying over the camp and that a committee of prisoners has taken charge had in the meantime spread throughout the whole camp. Our instructions, to remain calm and not to leave the barracks under any circumstances, were being conscientiously obeyed. In all the barracks the national representatives were depicting the situation in the camp and explaining the measures taken. But where are the Americans?
Haulot/Kuci, The Last Days of Dachau; Haulot was in the Dachau concentration camp, 1942-1945. KZ-Gst. Dachau

The night ... was extremely restless due to the sounds of war coming ever closer ... When I got to the main entrance of the camp at around 10:30am I came upon soldiers wearing their complete combat gear, and there was a white flag waving atop of one of the main towers ... A Mr. Lt. Wicker was the only officer from the camp with about 130 soldiers. I learned furthermore that all the officers, soldiers and officials had run off during the night. I spoke with Mr. Wicker up until the surrender of the camp. He was greatly inclined at first to desert along with his soldiers the large camp with its 35-40,000 inmates. I was able to prevent this ... I took a broomstick and attached a white cloth to it. I asked the German officer to accompany me and that is how we left the main gate of the concentration camp, many bullets whizzing by. A few moments later I saw a motorized American unit. By waving the white flag I was able to get their attention.

Report from Victor Maurer, representative of the Swiss Red Cross, on the surrender of the Dachau concentration camp to the Americans, May 18, 1945 (excerpt) ACICR

At about 15.00 on 29 April I arrived ... in Dachau... As we moved down along the west side of the concentration camp ... three people approached down the road under a flag of truce... These three people were a Swiss Red Cross representative and two SS troopers who said that they were the camp commander and the assistant camp commander and that they had come to the camp on the night of the 28th to take over from the regular camp personnel for the purpose of turning the camp over to the advancing Americans. The Swiss Red Cross representative acted as interpreter and stated that there were about 100 SS guards in the camp who had their arms stacked except for the people in the tower. He said that he had given instructions that there would be no shot fired and that it would take about 50 men to relieve the guards, as there were about 42,000 half-crazed prisoners of war in the camp, many of them typhus infected. He asked if I were an officer of the American army, to which I replied, "Yes, I am Assistant Division Commander of the 42nd Division and will accept the surrender of the camp in the name of the Rainbow Division of the American army."

Memorandum by Brigadier General Henning Linden to the Commanding General of the 42nd Division about the surrender of the Dachau concentration camp, May 2, 1945 (excerpt) Linden, Surrender

Commandant Heinrich Wicker and the Red Cross delegate Victor Maurer surrender the concentration camp to Brigadier General Henning Linden. With the white flag: the International Red Cross representative, Maurer, April 29, 1945. The negotiations took place in front of the gate to the SS camp. Photo: Raphael Algoet, ACICR

The gunfire ceased, and before long we caught sight of an American soldier holding a rifle. He took several steps from the gate, stopped, and looked about somewhat confused. Suddenly an avalanche of prisoners poured out onto the roll-call area. I joined them. First, they hugged the Americans and then tossed them into the air. A machine gun on Tower "B" opened fire, fatally wounding a Pole. Everyone ran towards the barracks for cover. It was about 5.15 pm.

Stanislav Zámečník, That was Dachau

What then followed is incredible. The whole camp presses against the fence. The SS men rounded up on the other side are openly mocked. If they fell into our hands, we would tear them apart. The mass roars its joy. Impossible to calm them. Only a few hours later, as darkness falls, is it possible to clear the camp entrance. Haulot, Lagertagebuch

View from Tower B of the prisoners greeting their liberators, April 29, 1945 Photo: Raphael Algoet, KZ-Gst. Dachau

SS camp command report on the roll-call count, April 29, 1945 ITS

```
Konzentrationslager Dachau

Der am 29.4.45 früh abgehaltene Zählappell
ergab folgenden Stand :

Lager                            27808
Revierpatienten                   4260
Revierpersonal                     267
G e s a m t                      32335

Männl.Häftlinge        31950
Weibl.(einschl.Kinder)   385

Im Laufe des 28.4.45 sind folgende Zugänge
ins Lager eingetroffen :

Enthymolog.Baracke                Männer Frauen
      "        "                     -      4
Obertraubing                        97      -
Standort-Verw.München               28      -
Allach                               2      -
Floßenbürg                           5      -
Arrest / K.A./                       2      -
Lebensborn                          27      -
Kaufering                         1602    167 +

G e s a m t - Zugänge             1763    171

A b g ä n g e :
Abgeschrieben wurden als verstorben  120

+ in der Zahl 167 weibl.Häftl.aus Kaufering
befinden sich 7 Frauen mit Kindern
```

Corpses piled up in front of the crematorium, April 29, 1945 The U.S. troops found almost 3,000 corpses upon entering the camp. Photo: NA Washington

In the crematorium morgue, April 29, 1945   NA Washington

View from Tower B of the prisoners greeting their liberators, April 29, 1945
Photo: Raphael Algoet, KZ-Gst. Dachau

Distributing bread on the camp road, April 30, 1945
Photo: Lee Miller, Lee Miller Archives, Chiddingly

After extensive study of sources and records, Stanislav Zámečník estimates that at least **41,566** persons died in the Dachau concentration camp.

32,099	dead are recorded by the International Tracing Service of the Red Cross in Arolsen.
9,467	additional deaths were proven on the basis of documents or the number of human remains in mass graves.
Total: 41,566	**deaths**

Included in this figure are the **4,000** Soviet prisoners of war shot in 1941 and 1942 (minimum estimate) and the **4,851** prisoners no longer able to work, who were murdered in the gas chambers at Hartheim or Auschwitz.

Unknown or presently undocumented is the number of dead in the following cases:

– Persons who individually or in groups were sent to the Dachau concentration camp for execution by the Gestapo as part of "special treatment" operations; they were not registered in the camp records.

– Persons who died in the subcamps or external work details after the registration of deaths had ceased (April 26, 1945) or in the course of the evacuation transports. The figures for these cases are far from complete.

– Prisoners unable to work who were transported from Dachau in 1944 to Lublin-Majdanek (1,000 persons) and Bergen-Belsen (1,400 persons) to be liquidated through starvation and inhumane treatment.

Dead prisoners, drawing by Zoran Mušič, a prisoner in the Dachau concentration camp from November 1944 to liberation. Moderna galerija Ljubljana

History after 1945

Repress and forget – that is how the attitude of the majority in West German society can be described in dealing with the legacy of the concentration camp. Soon after the war, very little on the grounds recalled the horrors of the years 1933-1945 in the former Dachau concentration camp. After the last survivors had left the grounds, the camp was first used as an internment camp, and then beginning in 1948 as a residential settlement for refugees. The former prisoners fought for the establishment of a memorial site, which was finally opened in 1965. Since then the Dachau Concentration Camp Memorial Site has been visited by more than 20 million people from almost every country in the world.

The immediate task after the liberation of the Dachau concentration camp and its subcamps was to provide for the more than 60,000 survivors and organize their repatriation. The typhus epidemic raging in the main camp had to be combated, the ill cared for, and several thousand corpses buried. At the end of July 1945, the last group of liberated prisoners left the former camp. For many of the Jewish survivors there was, however, no return home. Their relatives had been murdered, their livelihoods destroyed. The U.S. Army set up a separate DP camp for them (DP = Displaced Persons). Many of them were forced to remain in Germany for years before they could finally leave.

U.S. soldiers in a typhus ward set up in a barrack of the former concentration camp, April/May 1945 USHMM

US military rabbi David Eichhorn, delivering a sermon during the first public Sabbath service in the liberated camp, May 6, 1945 NA Washington

Dachau citizens view the crematorium on order of the U.S. military, May 7, 1945
The U.S. Army forced Dachau citizens to view the crematorium and the piles of corpses. Nazi party members were subsequently forced to help bury the dead. KZ-Gst. Dachau

Corpses being transported away from the crematorium for burial in mass graves on the Leitenberg, May 7-8, 1945 KZ-Gst. Dachau

Belgian prisoners departing for Brussels, May 26, 1945 Photo: Raphael Algoet, CEDGSC

After the war, the Allies established military courts to prosecute National Socialist crimes. An American military court was constituted in Dachau as early as the end of 1945. The trial conducted for crimes committed in the Dachau concentration camp became a model for subsequent trials. However, with the onset of the Cold War, the interest of the Americans in a thorough prosecution of Nazi crimes clearly diminished. In 1949, the West German judicial system assumed responsibility. Despite numerous preliminary proceedings, only a few prosecutions resulted. Except for murder, all other offences were soon amnestied or fell under the statute of limitations. Many crimes thus remained unpunished.

View of the dock during the first Dachau trial, 1945 NA Washington

Administration building of the American military court on the grounds of the former Dachau concentration camp, 1945/46 KZ-Gst. Dachau

Session of the U.S. Military court during the first Dachau trial, 1945 NA Washington

Execution of the former camp commandant Martin Weiss in the war criminals prison at Landsberg, May 28, 1946 NA Washington

The Dachau Internment Camp, 1945-1948

After the end of the war, the military government and the secret service of the U.S. Army (CIC) automatically arrested Nazi party functionaries, high-ranking bureaucrats and members of the SS. Internment Camp no. 29 was set up in the former Dachau concentration camp. Up to 25,000 prisoners were incarcerated here. American courts and German tribunals passed judgment on their personal responsibility for crimes committed under Nazism. From 1946, the internees' daily rations were mostly better than those of the civilian population. In connection with the escalating conflict between East and West, many internees were soon released.

Arrested members of the Nazi Party being transported to an internment camp, undated SV

Internees performing construction work in the Dachau internment camp, 1945 KZ-Gst. Dachau

Prisoners of the Dachau internment camp before their release, undated Photo: private ownership

In September 1948, the Bavarian Refugee Agency had the former prisoner camp reconstructed as a residential settlement for refugees and expelled ethnic Germans from eastern Europe. The residential settlement existed for almost 20 years and developed its own municipal infrastructure. The catastrophic housing shortage was used to justify this utilization of the former concentration camp. At the same time, however, it also showed the prevailing tendency to avoid dealing with the specific history of the camp.

"Dachau 1950 – once a horror – today no paradise", photo report about the Dachau residential settlement Quick, No. 18, April 30, 1950, BaySB

Residents of the residential settlement in front of the barracks on the camp road, undated KZ-Gst. Dachau

"We want to get out of the concentration camp barracks", banner on a partially demolished guard tower, September 1957 dpa

The Route to the Memorial Site

For the survivors, the fight against the repression and forgetting of what happened soon became a primary matter of concern. Many returned regularly to the former concentration camp site for commemorative services. After a first major international survivors' meeting in April 1955, those concerned now took up the battle to a have a worthy memorial site established.

14

French survivors commemorate their dead comrades at the liberated Dachau concentration camp, early May 1945 Agence France Presse, Paris

... And when we then go out together to Dachau during my next visit, perhaps the Hofgarten will be in bloom again and announce a new beginning for us as well.

Perhaps the barracks in the concentration camp will have then been vacated, and the present inhabitants have found more humane accommodation ... perhaps then the children in the "invalid barrack school" will be going to suitable schools and learn there who the old concentration campers were and how they got there, what we wanted and still want, perhaps they will then also be finally, finally taught that the murderers are the guilty ones – and not the murdered ...

Letter by Nico Rost to a German friend who was with him in the concentration camp, taken from, Ich war wieder in Dachau; Nico Rost was in the Dachau concentration camp, 1944-1945.

Corpses exhumed on the Leitenberg in Dachau, September 20, 1949
In August 1949, human remains were uncovered during excavation work on the Leitenberg. Press reports drew the attention of the international public to the neglect of the nearby concentration camp graves, which were exhumed in late September. KZ-Gst. Dachau

NICO ROST

ICH WAR WIEDER IN DACHAU

Official unveiling of the monument of the unknown prisoner in front of the crematorium, April 30, 1950
The choice of artist was controversial. Sculptor Fritz Koelle was initially persecuted by the National Socialists, before he came to terms with the Nazi regime and its official ideas on art. KZ-Gst. Dachau

The International Committee pursues the following goals:

a) Cultivation of memory ...

c) In agreement with the Bavarian government and other authorities to return the camp to the state it was in in 1945, and to establish there a documentation center and a museum.

d) The erection of a memorial

Statutes of the Comité International de Dachau, December 20, 1958 (excerpt) KZ-Gst. Dachau

Guard tower in 1957 Photo: dpa, 1957

Streit um Dachauer Krematorium

MÜNCHEN (SZ) — Die Schließung des Krematoriums im ehemaligen Konzentrationslager Dachau für den öffentlichen Besuch fordert ein Antrag, den der Landrat von Dachau, der CSU-Abgeordnete Heinrich Junker, im bayerischen Landtag eingebracht hat. Junker begründet seinen Antrag damit, man solle die weitere „Propaganda", in diesem Krematorium seien Opfer des Nationalsozialismus „vergast oder lebendig verbrannt worden", unterbinden. Die Organisation der ehemaligen Verfolgten in Bayern, der nichtkommunistische Landesrat für Freiheit und Recht, hat bereits angekündigt, er werde gegen diesen Antrag nachdrücklich Protest erheben. Nach einem weiteren Antra~ Junker soll auf dem KZ-Friedhof Dachau neben dem ~~~~~ auch ein Kre~~~~ zeic~~

"Dispute about the Dachau Crematorium", press report from the Süddeutsche Zeitung, July 20, 1955 (excerpt)

Opening of the first provisional exhibition organized by the Comité International de Dachau in the rooms of the large crematorium, 1960

Front right: Georges Walraeve, general secretary of the CID; next to him Dr. Alois Hundhammer, former Dachau prisoner and at the time deputy Minister President in Bavaria. Keystone

Demolition of the prisoners' barracks, November 14, 1962 All the barracks were torn down between 1962 and 1964. Dachauer Nachrichten, Fotoarchiv

Official dedication of the Catholic chapel "Mortal Agony of Christ", 1960
(architect Josef Wiedemann)
Around 50,000 people took part in the official dedication of the Mortal Agony of Christ chapel during the Eucharistic World Congress in August 1960. The construction of a chapel was initiated by priests who had survived their imprisonment in the concentration camp. The leadership of suffragan bishop and former "special prisoner" Johannes Neuhäusler was crucial in bringing their efforts to fruition. Karmel Kloster H. Blut

Announcement by the Bavarian State Finance Ministry about the construction of the memorial site in the former Dachau concentration camp, 1962 KZ-Gst. Dachau

Verlautbarung
des Bayer. Staatsministeriums der Finanzen
über die Ausgestaltung der Gedenkstätte
im ehemaligen KZ Dachau

Am 12. November 1962 fand im Bayer. Staatsministerium der Finanzen unter Vorsitz von Staatssekretär Dr. Lippert eine Besprechung mit dem Präsidenten des Internationalen Dachau-Komitees Dr. Albert Guérisse und weiteren Vertretern dieser Organisation über die Ausgestaltung der Gedenkstätte im ehemaligen KZ Dachau statt. Demnach wird mit der Errichtung des internationalen Mahnmals auf dem ehemaligen Appellplatz des Lagers in Kürze begonnen. Dieses Mahnmal war Gegenstand eines internationalen Wettbewerbs. Die Kosten wird das Komitee durch eine internationale Sammlung aufbringen.

Das ehemalige Wirtschaftsgebäude des Lagers hat der Freistaat Bayern zurückerworben. Es wird das Lagermuseum aufnehmen, das derzeit noch provisorisch im ehemaligen Krematorium untergebracht ist. Der Nordteil des Lagers soll ein Platz der Meditation werden; dort hat die katholische Kirche bereits die Todesangst-Christi-Kapelle errichtet. Von der evangelischen Kirche und dem israelitischen Landesverband werden im gleichen Bereich religiöse Gedenkstätten aufgeführt werden.

Der übrige Lagerbereich wird nach seiner Freimachung, die d-- Bayern bis Ende 1963 herbeiführen wird, als Ged-- beiden ersten Baracken am Appell-- liche übrige Baracken -- wurde--

Commemorative ceremony on the occasion of the 20th anniversary of the liberation of the Dachau concentration camp
On May 9, 1965, more than 4,000 former concentration camp prisoners commemorated the twentieth anniversary of liberation on the roll-call area of the former Dachau concentration camp.
Photo and press release: dpa, 1965

Guests of honor at the opening of the concentration camp memorial site on May 9, 1965
Seated from the left: 1. Dr. Alois Hundhammer, former concentration camp prisoner and chairman of the committee for the founding of the Dachau concentration camp memorial site, 4. Dr. Albert Guérisse, president of the Comité International de Dachau. KZ-Gst. Dachau

View of the 1965 exhibition KZ-Gst. Dachau

Individuals who played an important part in establishing the memorial site

The project to establish the Dachau memorial site was realized only after many years of committed effort on the part of survivors. Important to this achievement was the active involvement of the International Dachau Committee and the superb negotiating skills of its longtime president, Belgian general Albert Guérisse.
The committee received substantial assistance from a group of former persecutees in Bavaria, who joined forces to form a support council. The following members of this council rendered outstanding service to this project.

Alois Hundhammer (1900-1974)
Alois Hundhammer was a deputy of the Catholic Bavarian People's Party in the Bavarian state parliament since 1932. He was imprisoned in the Dachau concentration camp for a month in 1933. After 1945, Alois Hundhammer was one of the founders of the Christian Social Union (CSU). In 1959 he became chairman of the council supporting the establishment of a memorial site at Dachau. Keystone

Otto Kohlhofer (1915-1988)
Otto Kohlhofer was arrested in 1935 for distributing publications and flyers critical of the National Socialist regime. After serving a two and a half year prison sentence, he was sent to the Dachau concentration camp, where he was imprisoned until liberation. As longstanding chairman of the West German Dachau Camp Association and a member of the CID, he gradually assumed a key role in the struggle to establish a memorial site between 1955 and 1965. Photo: private ownership

Johannes Neuhäusler (1888-1973)
Johannes Neuhäusler came into conflict with the National Socialist regime early on. He was arrested in 1941 and taken to the Sachsenhausen concentration camp and later to Dachau. The SS held him in the bunker, isolated from the other prisoners, until liberation. In 1960 he became one of the most important supporters of the Dachau memorial site. AEMF

Ruth Jakusch (1914-1991)
Ruth Eisenberg, a Jewish resident of Frankfurt, returned to Germany as an interpreter for the U.S. Army. During the Dachau trials she met her future husband, Hugo Jakusch, a survivor who had spent twelve years imprisoned in the concentration camp. In 1962 she was commissioned by the CID to conduct research for the exhibition in the memorial site. Ruth Jakusch was the director of the memorial site until 1975. Photo: private ownership

Leonhard Roth (1904-1960)
The priest and Dominican friar Leonhard Roth was brought to the Dachau concentration camp in 1943, where he earned the respect of his fellow prisoners by working as a volunteer orderly for those infected with typhus. After liberation he remained in the camp, working as a priest and spiritual advisor for the interned SS guards. He was then active as a priest and advocate for the refugees who lived in the former prisoner barracks after 1948. As the delegate of the concentration camp priests to the CID, he fought for the establishment of a memorial site. KZ-Gst. Dachau

The memorial site was opened in 1965, and the international memorial on the former roll-call area was unveiled in 1968. The Bavarian government and the Comité International de Dachau signed an agreement establishing their future joint responsibility for the memorial site. In the 1970s and the 1980s, the memorial site developed increasingly into a place of learning and remembrance that found worldwide interest.

Aerial photo of the concentration camp memorial site, around 1969 KZ-Gst. Dachau

Seite 20 BERICHTE AUS BAYERN Montag, 9. September 1968 / Nr. 211

KZ-Häftlinge lösen ihr Versprechen ein

Mahnmal in Dachau enthüllt / Jugendliche Demonstranten stören die Feier / Sprechchöre und Transparente

Dachau (Eigener Bericht) — Mit einer Feier auf dem Appellplatz des ehemaligen Konzentrationslagers hat am Sonntagvormittag das Internationale Dachau-Komitee der 30 000 Häftlinge gedacht, die von den Nazis hier umgebracht worden sind. Dabei wurde das von dem jugoslawischen Bildhauer Glid Nandor geschaffene Denkmal enthüllt. Es besteht aus großen Betonflächen, zwischen denen ein geschlungener Weg in die Tiefe führt, und einer Skulptur von ineinander verflochtenen Bronze-Skeletten. Inschriften in vier Sprachen sind in das Denkmal eingemeißelt, das mit Spenden aus 23 Ländern finanziert wurde. An der Feier nahmen Delegationen ehemaliger Häftlinge aus vielen dieser Länder teil, auch aus der Tschechoslowakei. Die Veranstaltung verlief nicht ohne Störung.

Unmittelbar nach Beginn stürmten etwa 40, meist jugendliche Demonstranten aus einer Ecke auf den Platz, um mit Vietcongfahnen, einer roten Fahne und etwa einem Dutzend Transparenten mit verschiedenen Parolen die Versammlung daran zu erinnern, daß es auch heute noch politische Verfolgung und Konzentrationslager gebe. Der Protest richtete sich besonders gegen das Auftreten des Berliner Regierenden Bürgermeisters Schütz, der als Präsident des Bundesrats den Bundespräsidenten vertrat, und gegen den bayerischen Landwirtschaftsminister Hundhammer, in der Nazizeit selbst eine Zeitlang Häftling in Dachau.

Etwa auf halber Strecke zwischen der Ecke am Appellplatz und dem Rednerpult vor den beiden Tribünen traten Ordner des Dachau-Komitees, Polizisten und Teilnehmer der Veranstaltung den Protestierenden entgegen und drängen sie zurück. Dabei kam es zu Schlägereien mit Fäusten und Stöcken. Die meisten Transparente wurden zerstört, noch ehe die überwiegend ausländischen Besucher die zum Teil schwer verständlichen Parolen lesen konnten. Unter Sprechchören — „Ho Tschi-Minh", „Gegen NATO und Faschismus?", „Wo starb Benno Ohnesorg?", „Heute Dutschke, morgen wir!" — zogen

sich die Demonstranten wieder in ihre Ecke zurück. Dort wurden sie — unter einer roten Fahne der linksextremen Sozialistischen Deutschen Arbeiterjugend — von etwa 30 Landpolizeibeamten abgesperrt. Zahlreiche Photographen hielten die Szene fest. Dann wurden die Demonstranten von ehemaligen Häftlingen in leidenschaftliche Diskussionen verwickelt. Zu Tätlichkeiten kam es aber nicht mehr; die Feier ging eine Zeitlang ohne Sprechchöre weiter.

Sie hatte mit Signalen von Militärkapellen und dem Einmarsch von Ehrenkompanien der französischen, amerikanischen und belgischen Armee sowie der britischen Luftwaffe begonnen. Die Redner erinnerten daran, daß Konzentrationslager und Menschenvernichtung in der Welt noch kein Ende gefunden hätten, und daß der Friede immer neue Anstrengungen fordere. Minister Hundhammer versicherte seinen „ehemaligen Kameraden", wie er als antifaschistischer Kämpfer und einstiger KZ-Häftling sagen dürfe, daß der Geist im deutschen Volk ein anderer geworden sei, daß man aber Reste des Denkens von ehedem scharf beobachten müsse, vor allem, wenn dieses eine unerfahrene Jugend zu mobilisieren versuche.

„Menschenrechte bleiben weiter bedroht"

Dr. A. Guérisse, alias Pat O'Leary, der Präsident des Comiteé International de Dachau, das seinen Sitz in Brüssel hat, sagte, die ehemaligen Häftlinge würden diesen 8. September 1968 nicht vergessen. Er bringe ihnen die Einlösung des Versprechens, daß sie eines Tages in würdiger Form der Toten aus ihrer Gemeinschaft gedenken würden. Es dürfe aber niemals ein Vergessen für Menschen geben, die schuldlos und gewaltsam gestorben seien. Das Regime, das sich in Dachau selbst enthüllt habe, sei zwar 1945 ehrlos untergegangen. Doch sei der Friede nicht eingekehrt. 1968 gebe es noch immer Unrecht und Unterdrückung.

Gewerkschaften und Parteien, von Lagergemeinschaften anderer KZ, vom Ministerrat der DDR, dem USA-Arbeiter-Wohlfahrts-Fonds, der britischen Rheinarmee, der Israelitischen Kultusgemeinde, VVN-Organisationen, der Vereinigung sowjetischer Dachau-Veteranen, der Vereinigung griechischer Widerstandskämpfer, der Vereinigung Amnesty International (zur Befreiung politischer Häftlinge durch juristische Einzelaktionen und Druck öffentlicher Meinung und von vielen anderen Gruppen. An der Feier nahmen Prinz Bernhard der Niederlande sowie die Botschafter Norwegens, Italiens, Israels, Frankreichs, Belgiens, Österreichs, der Niederlande, Großbritanniens, Luxemburgs, der USA, Dänemarks, Jugoslawiens und Südafrikas teil.

Standortverwechslung

Während der Rede des Berliner Bürgermeisters Schütz lebte in der Ecke am Appellplatzes der Protest in Sprechchören wieder auf. „Schütz raus" und „Schütz — Faschist" wurde gerufen. Vielen Teilnehmern wurde erst durch Diskussionen mit den Demonstranten und im Gespräch auf der Tribüne der politische Standort der Protestierenden klar. Anfangs glaubten viele, es handle sich um eine Störung durch die NPD, zumal da die Transparente im Handgemenge schneller zerstört als gelesen worden waren.

Demonstranten erklärten, sie hätten sich ohne große Planung versammelt — unabhängige Studenten, Arbeiterjugend, SDS, —, um die Veranstaltung daran zu erinnern, daß es auch heute noch Konzentrationslager in Griechenland gebe, daß mit Kranzniederlegungen die Welt nicht besser werde, daß zu ihnen Leute sprächen, die „im Berlin durch Pogromhetze neue Verfolgung" vorbereiteten, daß die griechische Militärdiktatur von der NATO geschützt werde, während NATO-Detachements in Dachau zur Feier aufmarschierten. Einige Transparente enthüllten Inschriften, die mißverständlich bis provokatorisch wirken mußten, zum Beispiel: „Dachau grüßt Hitlers Erben". Das sollte sich ironisch auf Redner und Repräsentanten des Establishments beziehen, diente aber keineswegs der Bewußtseinsbildung, sondern führte überwiegend zur Verbitterung gegenüber den jungen Leuten.

DIE RAMPE DES TODES stellt das Mahnmal dar, das am gestrigen Sonntag auf dem Gelände des ehemaligen Konzentrationslagers Dachau enthüllt wurde. Photo: Kleine

Nur jeder 19. darf studieren

Zuwenig Plätze für Human- und Zahnmediziner an der Erlanger Universität

Erlangen (dpa) — Die Chance, an der Universität Erlangen-Nürnberg zum Studium der Humanmedizin oder der Zahnheilkunde zugelassen zu werden, steht für einen Abiturienten etwa wie 1:19. Wie aus Universitätskreisen zu erfahren war, muß ein Bewerber für die Zahnmedizin mindestens die Note 2,05 als Gesamtdurchschnitt der Abiturnoten und bei der Humanmedizin mindestens 2,3 haben, um angenommen zu werden. Ein Computer errechnet die „Rangliste" der Bewerber.

In Erlangen bewerben sich im kommenden Wintersemester 2330 Abiturienten um einen der 142 Plätze für das Medizinstudium und 880 um die zur Verfügung stehenden 27 Plätze für die Zahnheilkunde. An den anderen Universitäten in der Bundesrepublik liegen die Verhältnisse ähnlich: nur 2713 Plätze stehen für die 11 000 Erstsemester offen.

Um diesen gewaltigen Ansturm bewältigen zu können, ist in Hamburg eine Zentrale eingerichtet.

Es sei daher unumgänglich, den Naturwissenschaftlern räumlich und finanziell angemessene Arbeitsmöglichkeiten zu verschaffen.

Schulstreik angekündigt

Eltern gegen Reduzierung des Lehrpersonals

UFFENHEIM (dpa) — Aus Protest gegen den Abzug einer Lehrkraft treten die Eltern der Kinder des bisherigen vierklassigen Schulverbands...

Report on the unveiling of the international monument, Süddeutsche Zeitung, September 10, 1968
Above right: the monument's bronze sculpture The sculpture recalls human bodies entangled in barbed wire. Photo: Peter Brunner, 1995, KZ-Gst. Dachau

Detail from the plans for the monument: the prisoner patches, 1960
All of the prisoner categories were at first included in the plans. In the course of its realization however, the markings pink, green and black (homosexuals, "criminals", and "anti-socials") were left out. KZ-Gst. Dachau

Erection of the international monument on the former roll-call area of the concentration camp, 1967
The monument was created by sculptor Nandor Glid from Belgrade. He was the winner of an international competition conducted by the Comité International de Dachau. KZ-Gst. Dachau

Official opening of the Protestant Church of Reconciliation, Bishop Scharf at the handing over of the keys on May 2, 1967
This place of worship was built by the Protestant Church in Germany, with support from Protestant Christians from other countries in both eastern and western Europe, to remember the victims of National Socialism. It was placed into the care of the Bavarian Protestant Church.
Kurt Scharf was at this time Bishop of the Protestant Church in Berlin-Brandenburg and chairman of the Protestant Church Council in Germany. He had previously served as pastor at the Sachsenhausen concentration camp. Photo and press report: Keystone Agentur, Zurich, 1967

Official opening of the Jewish memorial building in Dachau on May 7, 1967
On the grounds of the former Dachau concentration camp the Jewish memorial building was officially opened in a ceremony on May 7, 1967 in the presence of numerous guests of honor and former concentration camp prisoners. It was built by the Israelite religious community in Bavaria to commemorate the approximately 6 million Jews who were murdered in the years of the National Socialist tyranny.
Our dpa photo: Rabbi David Spiro spoke the prayer for the dead (kaddish) in front of the memorial. Photo and press report: dpa, 1967

Israeli Foreign Minister Yitzak Rabin,
September 8, 1987 Photo: Niels Jörgensen, KZ-Gst. Dachau

A group of Sinti enter into a hunger strike against continuing discrimination, Good Friday 1980. The Sinti used the symbolism of the Dachau concentration camp to underscore the illegitimacy of the ongoing discrimination against them. Photo: Uschi Dresing, DZ Sinti und Roma

The Israeli Olympic delegation visited Dachau on September 1, 1972. Four days later terrorists murdered 11 of the Israeli athletes. dpa

Dachau survivor Adolf Maislinger points out a historic spot during a tour in the Dachau memorial site in the 1970s AMA

Abbreviations

BSV	Bratskoe Sotrudničestvo voennoplennych (resistance group formed by Soviet prisoners of war)
BVP	Bayerische Volkspartei (Bavarian People's Party)
Capo/Kapo	Concentration camp prisoner installed as a foreman of prisoner work detail
CIC	Counter Intelligence Corps (secret service branch of the U.S. Army)
CID	Comité International de Dachau
DAP	Deutsche Arbeiter Partei (German Workers' Party)
DAW	Deutsche Ausrüstungs-Werke (German Equipment Works)
DDP	Deutsche Demokratische Partei (German Democratic Party)
DHV	Deutschnationaler Handlungsgehilfen Verband (National Retail Clerks Association)
DNVP	Deutschnationale Volkspartei (German National People's Party)
DP	Displaced Person
Gestapo	Geheime Staatspolizei (secret state police)
K.L.D.	Konzentrationslager Dachau (Dachau concentration camp)
KA	Kommandanturarrest (detention)
KKE	Kommunistische Partei Griechenlands (Greek Communist Party)
KPD	Kommunistische Partei Deutschlands (German Communist Party)
NAZ	Neue Augsburger Zeitung ("Augsburg News")
NSDAP	Nationalsozialistische Deutsche Arbeiter Partei (National Socialist German Workers' Party)
O.C.	Organisation Consul (rightwing terror grouping in the Weimar Republic)
OHL	Oberste Heeresleitung (High Command of the German Armed Forces)
RFSS	Reichsführer SS (Reich leader of the SS)
RSHA	Reichssicherheitshauptamt (Reich Security Main Office)
RUDA	Tschechische Widerstandsgruppe (Czech resistance group)
SA	Sturmabteilung (storm troopers)
SD	Sicherheitsdienst (security service)
SIPO	Sicherheitspolizei (security police)
SIS	Special Intelligence Service
Slg.	Sammlung (collection)
SOE	Special Organizations Executive (British secret service)
SS	Schutzstaffel (protection squad)
Stapo	Staatspolizei (state police)
USPD	Unabhängige Sozialdemokratische Partei Deutschlands (Party of Independent Social Democracy, Germany)
WVHA/SS-WVHA	SS-Wirtschafts- und Verwaltungshauptamt (SS Economic and Administration Main Office)
z.b.V.	zur besonderen Verfügung (at special disposal)

Archive abbreviations (in catalogue)

ACICR	Les Archives du Comité international de la Croix-Rouge, Geneva
AdsD, Seliger-Archiv	Friedrich Ebert Stiftung Archiv der sozialen Demokratie – Seliger Archiv
AEMF	Archiv des Erzbistums Munich and Freising
AMA	Archiv der Münchner Arbeiterbewegung
BA Berlin	Bundesarchiv Berlin (Federal archives)
BA Koblenz	Bundesarchiv Koblenz (Federal archives)
BA Ludwigsburg	Bundesarchiv Ludwigsburg (Federal archives)
BA-MA	Bundesarchiv-Militärarchiv Freiburg (Federal & military archives)
BaPK	Bildarchiv Preuss. Kulturbesitz
BayHStA	Bayerisches Hauptstaatsarchiv (Bavarian state archives)
BaySB	Bayerische Staatsbibliothek (Bavarian state library)
BayStminJ	Bay. Staatsministerium der Justiz (Bavarian state justice ministry)
BHA	Bauhausarchiv – Museum für Gestaltung
CA Podol'sk	Centralnyj Archiv Ministerstvo Oborony RF, Podol'sk
CEDGSC	Centre d'Etudes et de Documentation Guerre et de Société contemporaine, Brussels
DHM	Deutsches Historisches Museum (German Historical Museum)
DÖW	Dokumentationszentrum österreichischer Widerstand (Document center of Austrian resistance)
DZ Oberer Kuhberg	Dokumentationszentrum Oberer Kuhberg
DZ Sinti und Roma	Dokumentations- und Kulturzentrum deutscher Sinti und Roma
FfZg	Forschungsstelle für Zeitgeschichte
FNDIRP	Fédération Nationale des Déportés et Internés, Résistants et Patriots, Paris
Gst. Alte Synagoge	Gedenkstätte Alte Synagoge Essen
Gst. Buchenwald	Gedenkstätte Buchenwald (Memorial Site Buchenwald)
HdBG	Haus der Bayerischen Geschichte (House of Bavarian History)
IfZ	Institut für Zeitgeschichte
ITS	International Tracing Service, Arolsen
IWM	Imperial War Museum
JM Frankfurt/Main	Jüdisches Museum Frankfurt/Main (Jewish Museum)
KZ-Gst. Dachau	KZ-Gedenkstätte Dachau (Dachau Concentration Camp Memorial Site)
KZ-Gst. Mittelbau-Dora	KZ-Gedenkstätte Mittelbau-Dora
KZ-Gst. Neuengamme	KZ-Gedenkstätte Neuengamme
LA Berlin	Landesarchiv Berlin – LA IV-Fotosammlung (photo collection, Berlin state archive)
LbDb Carls	Luftbilddatenbank Dr. Carls, Würzburg
MRD Besançon	Musée de la Résistance et de la Déportation, Besançon
Muzeum Auschwitz-Birkenau, Oświęcim	Państwowe Muzeum Auschwitz-Birkenau w Oświęcimiu;
Muzeum Majdanek	Państwowe Muzeum na Majdanku
NA Washington	National Archives at College Park
NIO	Nederlands Instituut voor Oorlogsdocumentatie
NwHStA Düsseldorf	Nordrhein-Westfälisches Hauptstaatsarchiv Düsseldorf
ÖNB	Österreichische Nationalbibliothek (National Library, Austria)
SAD	Standesamt Dachau (Dachau registry office)
SAH	Standesamt Hebertshausen (Hebertshausen registry office)
SAPMO	Stiftung Archiv der Parteien und Massenorganisationen der DDR im Bundesarchiv
Schweizerisches BA	Schweizerisches Bundesarchiv Bern (Swiss National Archive)
StA Bamberg	Staatsarchiv Bamberg (State archive)
StA München	Staatsarchiv Munich
StA Nürnberg	Staatsarchiv Nuremberg
StA Würzburg	Staatsarchiv Würzburg
StadtA Baden-Baden	Stadtarchiv Baden-Baden (City archive)
StadtA Dachau	Stadtarchiv Dachau
StadtA Landsberg am Lech	Stadtarchiv Landsberg am Lech
StadtA Mühldorf am Inn	Stadtarchiv Mühldorf am Inn
StadtA München	Stadtarchiv Munich
StadtA Nürnberg	Stadtarchiv Nuremberg
StadtA Würzburg	Stadtarchiv Würzburg
SUAP	Statni ustredni archiv Praze (Central State Archives, Prague)
SV	Südd.Verlag – Bilderdienst
UB	Ullstein Bilderdienst
USHMM	US Holocaust Memorial Museum, Photo Archives
VGAb	Verein für Geschichte der Arbeiterbewegung
WGZJ	Wachturm Gesellschaft der Zeugen Jehovas (Watchtower Society of Jehovah's Witnesses)
Yad Vashem	Yad Vashem, Jerusalem

Loans (for the exhibition)

We would like to express our thanks to the following for making available loans and copies for reproduction:

Archiv der Gedenkstätte Mauthausen;
Archiv der Münchner Arbeiterbewegung;
Archiv der sozialen Demokratie der Friedrich-Ebert-Stiftung, Bonn;
Archiv der Stiftung Reichspräsident Friedrich-Ebert-Gedenkstätte, Heidelberg;
Archiv des Erzbistums München und Freising;
Archiv Walter Simon, Nuremberg;
Archives Nationales, Paris;
Archiwum Głównej Komisji Badania Zbrodni Przeciwko Narodowi Polskiemu, Państwowy Instytut Naukowy
Arhiv Vojvodine, Novi Sad;
Asklepios Lungenfachkliniken Gauting;
Auswärtiges Amt Berlin – Politisches Archiv;

Bauhausarchiv – Museum für Gestaltung, Berlin;
Bayerische Staatsbibliothek, Munich;
Bayerische Verwaltung Staatliche Schlösser, Gärten und Seen – Liegenschaftsverwaltung;
Bayerisches Hauptstaatsarchiv, Munich;
Bayerisches Hauptstaatsarchiv – Kriegsarchiv, Munich;
Bayerisches Staatsministerium der Justiz, Munich;
Bildarchiv Preußischer Kulturbesitz, Berlin;
Bundesarchiv – Militärarchiv Freiburg;
Bundesarchiv Berlin; Bundesarchiv, Außenstelle Ludwigsburg;
Bundesarchiv, Koblenz;

Centralnyj Archiv Ministerstvo Oborony RF, Podol'sk;
Centre de Documentation Juive Contemporaine, Paris;

Deutsche Dienststelle – Wehrmachtsauskunftsstelle, Berlin;
Deutsche Schillergesellschaft, Marbach am Neckar;
Deutsches Filminstitut-DIF, Frankfurt;
Deutsches Historisches Museum, Berlin;
Deutsches Rotes Kreuz – Suchdienst, Munich;
Deutsches Rundfunkarchiv Frankfurt;
Deutsches Rundfunkarchiv Potsdam;
Dokumentations- und Kulturzentrum deutscher Sinti und Roma, Heidelberg;
Dokumentationsarchiv des österreichischen Widerstandes, Vienna;
Dokumentationszentrum ehemaliges Reichsparteitagsgelände, Nuremberg;
Dokumentationszentrum Oberer Kuhberg, Ulm;

Forschungsstelle für Zeitgeschichte, Hamburg;
Foto Sessner, Dachau;
Fritz Bauer Institut, Frankfurt;

Gedenkstätte Alte Synagoge Essen;
Gedenkstätte Buchenwald;
Gedenkstätte Deutscher Widerstand, Berlin;
Gedenkstätte und Museum Sachsenhausen;
Geheimes Staatsarchiv Preußischer Kulturbesitz, Berlin;
General Consulate of the Republic of Croatia;

Hessisches Hauptstaatsarchiv, Wiesbaden;
Hessisches Landesmuseum, Darmstadt;
Imperial War Museum, London;
Institut für Zeitgeschichte, Munich;
Institute of Contemporary History and Wiener Library, London;
International Tracing Service, Arolsen;
Israelitische Kultusgemeinde Nuremberg;

Jüdisches Museum Frankfurt;

Katholische-Arbeitnehmer-Bewegung – Diözesanverband Augsburg;
Kloster St. Ottilien;
Kreismuseum Mühldorf;
Kreismuseum Wewelsburg;
KZ-Gedenkstätte Flossenbürg;
KZ-Gedenkstätte Neuengamme;

Landesarchiv Berlin;
Leo Baeck Institute, New York;
Les Archives du Comité international de la Croix-Rouge, Geneva;
Library of Congress, Washington D.C.;
Ludwig-Maximilians-Universität München – Institut für Vor- und Frühgeschichte;

Luftbilddatenbank Ing. Büro Dr. Carls, Würzburg;

Mahn- und Gedenkstätte zum KZ Lichtenburg;
Militärgeschichtliches Forschungsamt, Hamburg;
Musée de la Résistance et de la Déportation, Besançon;
Musée National d'Art Moderne, Paris;
Museum of Jewish Heritage, New York;
Muzeum mesta Brna;

National Archives, Washington D.C.;
Nederlands Instituut voor Oorlogsdocumentatie, Amsterdam;
New York Public Library – Dorot Jewish Division;
Nordrhein-Westfälisches Hauptstaatsarchiv, Düsseldorf;

Österreichische Gesellschaft für Zeitgeschichte – Bildarchiv, Vienna;
Österreichische Nationalbibliothek, Vienna;

Państwowe Muzeum Auschwitz-Birkenau w Oświęcimiu;
Państwowe Muzeum na Majdanku;
Państwowe Muzeum Stutthof;
Państwowe Instytut Naukowy – Instytut Śląski w Opolu;
Pfarramt Heilig Kreuz, Dachau;
Public Records Office, London;

Sammlung Karl Stehle, Munich;
Sammlung Rudolf Herz, Munich;
Seliger Archiv im Archiv der sozialen Demokratie der Friedrich-Ebert-Stiftung, Bonn;
Serbisch-Orthodoxe Diözese, Munich;
Simon Wiesenthal Center, Los Angeles;
Staatsarchiv Bamberg;
Staatsarchiv Munich;
Staatsarchiv Nuremberg;

Loans (for the exhibition)

Staatsarchiv Würzburg;
Staatsbibliothek Augsburg;
Stadtarchiv Baden-Baden;
Stadtarchiv Bamberg;
Stadtarchiv Dachau;
Stadtarchiv Munich;
Stadtarchiv Nuremberg;
Stadtarchiv Würzburg;
Stadtbücherei Landsberg;
Stadtmuseum Munich;
Standesamt Dachau;
Standesamt Hebertshausen;
Státní Ústřední Archiv, Prague;
Stiftung Brandenburgische Gedenkstätten – Mahn- und Gedenkstätte Ravensbrück;
Stiftung sächsischer Gedenkstätten, Dresden;
SV-Bilderdienst, Munich;

The Jewish Museum, New York;
Thüringisches Hauptstaatsarchiv, Weimar;

Ullstein Bilderdienst, Berlin;
UN Archives and Records Management Section – Archives and Records Center, New York;
US Holocaust Memorial Museum Washington D.C.;
US General Consulate, Munich;

Verein für Geschichte der Arbeiterbewegung, Vienna;

Wachtturm-Gesellschaft, Geschichtsarchiv, Selters/Ts.;

Yad Vashem – The Martyrs' and Heroes' Remembrance Authority, Jerusalem;
YIVO Institute, New York;

Żydowski Instytut Historyczny, Warsaw

For their help and advice we would like to thank:
Lydia Abel, Anna Andlauer, Waldemar Ball, Ferdinand Berger, Eva Bernadova, Tadeusz Biernacki, Ludwig Bloch, Franz Brückl, Michel Daval, Wolfgang David, André Delpech, Leonard Dinnerstein, Ferdinand Dupuis, Lucille Eichengreen, Kerstin Engelhardt, Anne Erbacher-Serantis, Ladislaus Ervin-Deutsch, Marco Esseling, Ulrich Fackler, Edmond Falkuss, Vladimír Feirabend, Josef Felder, Heinz Feldheim, Franz Fichtl, Karola Fings, Josef Fucht, Anita Garibaldi, Hans Gasparitsch, Erwin Gebhard, Ursula Geier, Albert Geiregeat, Christo Georgiew, Sabine Gerhardus, Waldemar Ginsburg, Jefimas Glikas, Irma Göhring, Anton Gortnar, Luise Gostner, Janez Ivo Gregorc, Michaela Haibl, Judith Hart, Arthur Haulot, Josef R. Hausner, Armin Heigl, Peter Heilmann, Dorothea Heiser, Manfred Hirschberg, Iris Hofer, Robert Hofmann, Richard Hundhammer, Christl Hunner, Anton Jež, Anton Jilek, Helene Joringer, Hermann Kaienburg, Ravil' Kasapov, Paul Kerstenne, Werner Kleeman, Sadija Klepo, Franz-Xaver Klingseisen, Viktor Alexandrowitsch Kononenko, Gabi Krynitzky, Sylvester Kukuła, Branko Kukurin, Karl Kunkel, Hans Landauer, Toni Lane, Nikolaus Lehner, Albert Lörcher, Steven Maitinsky, Max Mannheimer, Bernhard Marks, Hubert Mattischek, Jörg Mehrwerth, Clemens Mennicken, J.V. Mesdag, Pierre Metzger, Andrea Miller, Albert Montal, Franz Mörtl, Gertraud Mörtl, Zoran Music, Falk Ohorn, Franz Olah, Karl Ostermayer, Reinhard Otto, Kristian Ottosen, Reinhard Papenfuß, Hildegard Pickers, Giuseppe Pini, Jurij Piskunow, Friedrich Popp, Anna Pröll, Hildegard Quaeck, Undine Quaeck, Alois Raths, Zygmunt Raźniewski, W.G. Reijntjes, Ingmar Reither, Hans-Günther Richardi, Dirk Riedel, Karl Riemer, Roger Robach, Wolfgang F. Robinow, Sigrid Rohde, Ingeborga Rosenbusch, Karl Heinz Roth, Hubert Roussel, Joseph Rovan, Krystyna Rudolf, Friedrich Schafranek, Hermann Scheipers, Pierre Schillio, Lilli Schlumberger-Dogu, Georg Schmitz, Michael Schneeberger, Thomas Schrom, Coco Schumann, David Schuster, Willy Sel, Stane Šinkovec, Jerzy Skrzypzek, Johannes Sonnenschein, Leszek Stanowski, Ludwig Stark, Eva Strauß, Stefan Szulak, Hans Taschner, Albert Theis, Ivan Trinastić, Daniela Uher, Miroslav Ulc, Stane Ursiè, Francesca Vergan, Hilde Wagner, Ursula Wamser, Wilfried Weinke, Karl Weller, Piotr Wodnik, Elisabeth M. Yavnai, Beate Zainer, Stanislav Zámečník

Literature

Adam, Walter, Nacht über Deutschland, 1947.

Bayle, François, Croix gammée contre caducée. Les expériences humaines en Allemagne pendant la deuxième guerre mondiale, self-published 1950.
Beimler, Hans, Im Mörderlager Dachau. Vier Wochen in den Händen der braunen Banditen, Berlin 1980.
Bernard, Jean, Pfarrerblock 25487, Luxemburg 1987.
Biskupski, Księża polscy w niemieckich obozach koncetracyjnych, London 1946.
Brodski, J. A., Živyje Borjutsja, Moscow 1965.
Burkhard, Hugo, Tanz mal Jude, Nuremberg 1966.

dtv-Atlas zur Weltgeschichte.
(ed.) Werner Hilgemann and Hermann Kinder, vol. II: Von der Französischen Revolution bis zur Gegenwart, Munich [26]1992.

Ervin-Deutsch, Ladislaus, About Those who survived and Those who Died. From Auschwitz to Labour Camp III Kaufering, in: Dachau and Nazi Terror I/2002.

Falkuss, Edmond, Zeitzeugen-Interview, HdBG Augsburg 2000.
Feuerbach, Walter (pseudonym of Walter Ferber), 55 Monate Dachau, Luzern 1945.
Fraenkel, Ernst, Der Doppelstaat, Hamburg 2001.
Fremund, Dr. Karel and Král, Dr. Václav, (ed.), Die Vergangenheit warnt, Prague 1960.

Grand, Anselm, Turm A ohne Neuigkeit, Vienna/Leipzig 1946.

Haulot, Arthur, Lagertagebuch Januar 1943 – Juni 1945, in: Dachauer Hefte 1/1985.
Haulot, Arthur/**Kuci,** Ali, Die letzten Tage von Dachau, 1945.
Himmler, Heinrich, Geheimreden 1933 bis 1945, Berlin 1974.
Holzhaider, Hans, Die Sechs vom Rathausplatz, Munich 1982.
Hübsch, Alfred, Die Insel der Standrechts, manuscript.

Jež, Anton, Der Stollen war unser Unglück und unser Glück. Erinnerungen an das KZ-Außenkommando Überlingen/Aufkirch, in: Dachauer Hefte 15/1999.

Kalmar, Rudolf, Zeit ohne Gnade, Vienna 1946.
Kašák, Karel, Die Aufzeichnungen von Karel Kašák, compiled, commented and footnoted by Stanislav Zámečník, in: Dachauer Hefte 11/1995.
Kulka, Erich, in: Pingel, Falk, Häftlinge unter SS-Herrschaft, Hamburg 1978.
Kupfer-Koberwitz, Edgar, Die Dachauer Tagebücher, Munich 1997, entry of December 13 1943.
Kupfer-Koberwitz, Edgar, Die Mächtigen und die Hilflosen. Als Häftling in Dachau, vol. I: Wie es begann, Stuttgart 1957.

Langbein, Hermann, ... nicht wie die Schafe zur Schlachtbank, Frankfurt/M. 1980.
Langbein, Hermann, … wir haben es getan, 1964.
Linden, J. Henning, Surrender, Elm Grove, WI, 1997.
Lustig, Oliver, KZ Wörterbuch, Bucharest 1987.

Majdański, Kazimierz, Ihr werdet meine Zeugen sein, Mittelbiberach 1995.
Malá, Irena/Kubátová, Ludmila, Pochody smrti, Prague 1965.
Mannheimer, Max, Theresienstadt – Auschwitz – Warsaw – Dachau. Recollections, in: Dachau and the Nazi Terror I/2002.
Matejka, Viktor, Widerstand ist Alles. Notizen eines Unorthodoxen, Vienna 1984.
Mein Schatten in Dachau, (ed.) Comité International de Dachau, compiled and commented by Dorothea Heiser, Munich 1993.
Mladenović, Memoari Patriarha Srpskog Gavrila, 1990.
Möller, Horst, Weimar. Die unvollendete Demokratie, Munich [2]1987.
Musiol, Dachau 1933-1945, Kratowice 1968.

Najnigier, Powrot z daleka, Warsaw 1973.

Pingel, Falk, Häftlinge unter SS-Herrschaft, Hamburg 1978.
Popp, Hans, Ein weiterer Transport nach Dachau. Mitteilungsblatt der Lagergemeinschaft Dachau, 1963.

Reichsführer! Briefe von und an Himmler. (ed.) H. Heiber, Stuttgart 1968.
Riemer, Hermann E., Sturz ins Dunkel, Munich 1947.

Rost, Nico, Goethe in Dachau. Literatur und Wirklichkeit, Munich 1946.
Rost, Nico, Ich war wieder in Dachau, 1956.

Schätzle, Julius, Wir klagen an. Ein Bericht über den Kampf, das Leiden und das Sterben in deutschen Konzentrationslagern, Stuttgart 1946.
Schecher, Karl Ludwig, Rückblick auf Dachau. Unpublished account from the 1960s, KZ-Gst. Dachau.
Schulze, Hagen, Weimar. Deutschland 1917-1933, 1998.
Schwake, Gregor, Kirchenmusik im Konzentrationslager Dachau, in: Der Chorwächter. Zeitschrift für Kirchenmusik, LXXI. Jg./1946.
Šinkovec, Stane, Dachau Zbornik, Ljubljana 1981.
Speer, Albert, Der Sklavenstaat. Meine Auseinandersetzungen mit der SS, Stuttgart 1981.

Todeslager Sachsenhausen. Ein Dokumentarbericht vom Sachsenhausenprozeß. Berlin 1948.
Tuchel, Johannes, Inspektion der Konzentrationslager 1938-1945, Boppard 1994.
Tuvel Bernstein, Sara, Die Näherin. Erinnerungen einer Überlebenden, Munich/Vienna 1998.

Verfolgung, Vertreibung, Vernichtung, (ed.) Kurt Pätzold, Leipzig 1983.

Wagner, A., Karte Todesmarsch.

Zámečník, Stanislav, That was Dachau 1933-1945, Paris 2004.

Institutions and persons involved in the redesign and renewal of the Dachau Concentration Camp Memorial Site

Comité International de Dachau
Dr. h.c. Max Mannheimer
Albert Theis
Dr. Stanislav Zámečník

Central State Office for Civic Education (overall direction)
Dr. Michael Rupp
Dr. Peter März
Dr. Zdenek Zofka

The Dachau Concentration Camp Memorial Site
Dr. h.c. Barbara Distel
Dr. Gabriele Hammermann

Staatliches Hochbauamt Freising (building measures)
Ernst Baumann
Wolfgang Vogl

House of Bavarian History
Dr. habil. Ludwig Eiber
Thomas Felsenstein
Prof. Dr. Claus Grimm
Dr. Christoph Henzler
Michael Neher
Christian Schölzel M.A.
Dr. Manfred Treml

Expert advisory board (as of 1994)
Prof. Dr. Wolfgang Benz (chairman)
Dr. Hellmuth Auerbach
Dr. Stefanie Endlich
Prof. Dr. Karl Filser
Ministerialrat Manfred Förster
Dr. Detlef Garbe
Prof. Dr. Hans Günter Hockerts
Dr. Otto Lohr
Dr. h.c. Max Mannheimer
Dipl.-Ing. Giulio Marano
Dr. habil. Hartmut Mehringer
Prof. Dr. Dipl.-Ing. Winfried Nerdinger
Dr. Hans-Uwe Rump
Prof. Dr. Chaim Schatzker
Albert Theis
Dr. Manfred Treml
Dr. Bernd Vollmar
Dr. Stanislav Zámečník
Dr. Jürgen Zarusky

Exhibition

Project direction
House of Bavarian History
Dr. Manfred Treml (until July 2000)
Prof. Dr. Claus Grimm (from August 2000)
Dr. Ludwig Eiber

Contributors
Dr. h.c. Barbara Distel
Dr. Ludwig Eiber
Dr. Gabriele Hammermann
Dr. Christoph Henzler
Michael Neher
Christian Schölzel
Dr. Stanislav Zámečník
Dr. Zdenek Zofka

Assistance
Wolfgang Kucera M.A.
Paul Martin M.A.
Christoph Riedelsheimer
Sylvia Stegmüller M.A.

Translators
Paul Bowman
Miriamne Fields
Graham Pascoe

Design
Kleineberg & Partner, Braunschweig (framework conception, design of exhibition elements)
Hinz & Kunst, Braunschweig (graphic conception)

Fritz Armbruster (realization and construction)
Wolfgang Felber (graphic realization, cartography, graphics)
Claudia Geier (assistant)
Peh & Schefoik (large maps)
»sehen und verstehen« Modellbau Peter Götz (model construction)
multimedia-authoring Dr. Robert Hofmann (PC stations)
Chronik Videoproduktion Georg Schmidbauer (eyewitness interviews and films)
media connect Multimedia Erich Geiersberger (audio stations)
Print- und Mediacenter Ledin (print)

Imprint

**Catalogue for the exhibtion
"The Dachau Concentration Camp 1933-1945",**
conceived and realized by the House of
Bavarian History in cooperation with the expert
advisory board for the new design of the
Dachau Concentration Camp Memorial Site, the
Comité International de Dachau and the
Dachau Concentration Camp Memorial Site.

Published by:
© 2005, Comité International de Dachau;
Barbara Distel, Dachau Concentration Camp
Memorial Site

Editorial team:
Barbara Distel, Gabriele Hammermann,
Stanislav Zámečník, Jürgen Zarusky, Zdenek Zofka

Translation into English:
Paul Bowman, Berlin

Proof-reading: Veronika Stroh, Dirk Riedel

A detailed listing of the archival shelf marks for
the individual exhibition objects is located at the
House of Bavarian History, Augsburg

Design and setting:
Bruno Schachtner, Grafik-Werkstatt, Dachau

Print and distribution: Edition Lipp Verlagsgesellschaft mbH, Munich

5. Edition

ISBN 978-3-87490-751-4

www.comiteinternationaldachau.com